by Brooke C. Stoddard

Series developed by Peggy Schmidt

A New Century Communications Book

Other titles in this series include:

CARS
COMPUTERS
EMERGENCIES
ENTERTAINMENT
FASHION
FITNESS
HEALTH CARE
KIDS
MONEY
MUSIC
OFFICE
SPORTS
TRAVEL

Library of Congress Cataloging-in-Publication Data

Stoddard, Brooke C.
Building / by Brooke C. Stoddard.
p. cm. — (Careers without college)
"A New Century Communications book."
ISBN 1-56079-388-0 (pbk.) : $7.95
1. Construction industry — Vocational guidance — United States.
2. Building trades — Vocational guidance — United States. 3. High school graduates — Employment — United States. I. Title. II. Series.
HD9715.U52S767 1994
690'.023'73—dc20 94-17766
CIP

Art direction: Linda Huber
Cover photo: Bryce Flynn Photography
Cover and interior design: Greg Wozney Design, Inc.
Composition: Book Publishing Enterprises, Inc.
Printed in the United States of America
10 9 8 7 6 5 4 3 2 1

Text photo credits
Color photo graphics: J. Gerard Smith Photography
Page xiv: © The Image Bank/Kuhn, Inc.
Page 16: © Photo Edit/Richard Hutchings
Page 30: © Photo Edit/Tony Freeman
Page 46: © Photo Edit/Mary Kate Denny
Page 62: © Photo Edit/Tom McCarthy

ABOUT THIS SERIES

Careers without College is designed to help those who don't have a four-year college degree (and don't plan on getting one any time soon) find a career that fits their interests, talents and personality. It's for you if you're about to choose your career—or if you're planning to change careers and don't want to invest a lot of time or money in more education or training, at least not right at the start.

Some of the jobs featured do require an associate degree; others require only on-the-job training that may take a year, several months or only a few weeks. In today's increasingly competitive job market, you may want to eventually consider getting a two- or maybe a four-year college degree to move up in a field.

Each title in the series features five jobs in a particular industry or career area. Some of them are "ordinary," others are glamorous. The competition to get into certain featured occupations is intense; as a balance, we have selected jobs under the same career umbrella that are easier to enter. Some of the other job opportunities within each field will be featured in future titles in this series.

Careers without College has up-to-date information that comes from extensive interviews with experts in each field. The format of each book is designed for easy reading. Plus, each book gives you something unique: an insider's look at the featured jobs through interviews with people who work in them now.

We invite your comments about the series, which will help us with future titles. Please send your correspondence to: Careers without College, c/o Peterson's, P.O. Box 2123, Princeton, NJ 08543-2123.

Peggy Schmidt has written about education and careers for 20 years. She is author of Peterson's best-selling *The 90-Minute Resume.*

ACKNOWLEDGMENTS

Many thanks to the following people for their contributions to this book:

James Kenny, Chairman of the Apprenticeship Committee, National Association of Plumbing-Heating-Cooling Contractors, Falls Church, Virginia

Robert Krul, Apprenticeship Coordinator, United Union of Roofers, Waterproofers and Allied Workers, Washington, D.C.

Gene Natole, Apprentice Coordinator, Bricklayers and Allied Craftsmen, Local 5, Edison, New Jersey

A. J. Pearson, IBEW-NECA National Joint Apprenticeship Committee, Upper Marlboro, Maryland

Dennis Scott, Technical Director, Apprenticeship and Training Department, United Brotherhood of Carpenters and Joiners of America, Washington, D.C.

Roger Sheldon, retired Communications Director, United Brotherhood of Carpenters and Joiners of America, Washington, D.C.

Eugene Stinner, National Training Coordinator, International Masonry Institute, Washington, D.C.

Dennis Torbett, Director for Apprentice Programs, Home Builders Institute, Washington, D.C.

Andy Wermes, Apprenticeship and Training, United Brotherhood of Carpenters and Joiners of America, Washington, D.C.

WHAT'S IN THIS BOOK

Why These Building Trades? vi

Steve Thomas on Finding Your Place in the World of Construction viii

Success Stories xiii

Carpenter 1

Electrician 17

Plumber 31

Mason 47

Roofer/Waterproofer 63

More Information Please 77

Will You Fit into the Building World? 80

About the Author 86

WHY THESE BUILDING TRADES?

Since civilization began, people have had a special regard for those who erected the buildings in which they lived, worked and worshiped. Passersby still stop to peer through holes in wooden fences to watch workers building a new structure.

Building requires the skills of many tradespeople, but central to nearly all construction is the work of the craftspeople featured in this book. To get into these jobs, you don't need a college degree, but you do need aptitude, enthusiasm and a willingness to learn and work hard. These five trades are:

- ❑ carpenter
- ❑ electrician
- ❑ plumber
- ❑ mason
- ❑ roofer/waterproofer

Each trade has formal and informal training programs. The formal apprenticeship programs result in a "journeyman" certificate honored by employers everywhere. Apprenticeship programs can be union or non-union; graduating from a union program does not limit you to working for union-only employers, nor does graduating from a non-union program mean you cannot apply for and get union membership.

Carpenters are involved in virtually every construction project. They put up the walls and the roofs and install the doors, the windows, the cabinets and shelves and more. Because their work may start with the foundation and end with interior finishing, they often coordinate and schedule the work of other tradespeople.

Electricians bring the "magic" of electricity—lights, heating and cooling and telecommunications—to a building. Not only do they do the familiar wiring of houses and office buildings but they also build power stations, attach cables to the high-tension towers stretching from city to city and wire the sound booths of music studios.

Plumbers lay the pipes that bring us water and dispose of wastewater. They are experts at joining pipe, whether it's copper, steel, plastic or iron. Wherever pipes are needed—in a brewery or skyscraper or new bathroom for the home—plumbers are there.

The materials masons work with—concrete, brick, stone and ceramic tile—are enduring and can be shaped into works of great beauty. Whether it's building a chimney or installing marble on the side of a skyscraper, masons create works of art big and small.

The work of roofers and waterproofers is critical; unless water is kept out of buildings, they will deteriorate. Waterproofers make sure groundwater cannot seep into underground walls. Roofers fasten down wood, metal, tile or even rubber and asphalt coating to thwart water no matter how it may arrive—by drizzle or by hurricane.

Thousands of skilled journeymen—both men and women—have gone into business for themselves. Competition is often tough, but those who have "become their own boss" can live a dream that's not available to people in many careers.

STEVE THOMAS

on Finding Your Place in the World of Construction

Steve Thomas has combined his carpentry, sailing, writing and on-camera skills to create several careers. He is best known as the host of the Public Broadcasting System program *This Old House,* which features old-home renovation.

Thomas himself is a skilled renovator. His father taught him carpentry skills as a youngster. When he went to college in Olympia, Washington, he worked as a housepainter.

After college Thomas worked as a carpenter, and he and his partner bought a house that they fixed up and sold. His partner continued in the business, but Thomas traveled to Europe, where he helped build and sail boats.

It was sailing, in fact, that brought Thomas to television. He wrote a book about his experiences with Mau Pialug, a Micronesian who taught Thomas how to navigate using only waves, stars and birds. The book spawned a PBS television show, *The Last Navigator,* in 1989. That same year, he became the host of *This Old House.*

Out of his *This Old House* experience came two more books. The first, *This Old House Kitchens,* was published in 1992. *This Old House Baths* followed in 1993. Thomas is currently working on two new books: a third in the *This Old House* series, on exterior renovation, and one entitled *Four Whales for Tigara,* about his adventures in the Alaskan Arctic.

Thomas has renovated a number of his own houses, including an 1846 Greek Revival house and the 1836 Georgian-style home in which he currently lives with his wife and family in the Boston area. He shared these thoughts about going into building as a career.

As a boy I was always very interested in construction, building and renovation. It runs in the family. My grandfather was a missionary in the Alaskan Arctic and had to make his own dogsleds, houses and cabins. My father bought fixer-upper houses, and we were always working on them.

Some of my earliest memories are of planing a piece of wood. I think there is nothing more satisfying than watching the curl of pinewood rising from a plane and smelling the scent that's released.

So in a way I've been working on houses all my life. Now, when I'm doing a full renovation on a home, I choose the part of it I know I can tackle—usually the carpentry—and leave the rest to the other experts—plumbers, electricians, plasterers and heating and cooling specialists. As I advise the viewers of *This Old House,* you can't do it all, so it's better to be good at one thing. Choose a discipline, master it and then branch out.

I've always had a great respect for people who are skilled in construction. On *This Old House* we try to reveal their craftsmanship—the fine points of their skills that people might take for granted because they don't understand the inner workings of the craft.

Most craftsmen and craftswomen take a great deal of personal pride in their work. We recently renovated a 1907 shingle-style Victorian house on the show. Our carpenter spent a lot of time restoring the details on the front of the home to what he thought they were when the house was built. Some of this work was not specified in his contract with the homeowners, but he couldn't stand the thought of not doing the job right.

This is the job of a true craftsman—doing the extra bits to get the job right regardless of the pay received. I've been with craftspeople as they drove by their jobs ten years later and heard them say with pride, "I'm glad I did that extra bit of work because the house really looks right." It pays off too. The world is increasingly competitive, and reputation counts for a lot in getting work.

All the trades have challenges and rewards. I recently saw some clever electrical work in an 1830s house built in what is called post-and-beam construction. Massive posts and beams buried in the walls make it tough to retrofit electrical wiring without destroying the finished walls or trim. But this electrician's knowledge of the old construction style allowed him to route the wires very cleverly. Renovation is especially challenging to electricians and plumbers when historic details need to be preserved.

I've been impressed, too, by masons I've watched working on our show. They not only have to be very good at their skills, such as reconstructing old fireplaces and chimneys, but they must be familiar with the construction techniques and aesthetics of the old styles. Renovation is an increasingly large portion of total construction in this country, so this kind of knowledge helps keep masons busy.

We recently saw some excellent roofing craftsmanship as well. On the shingle-style Victorian I mentioned earlier, the roofers ripped off the old asphalt shingle roof, which was not historically appropriate, and installed a red cedar shingle roof. The house has some really challenging details: two turrets, a big central chimney and even a gracefully curved "eyebrow" window. But these roofers were real pros, and they did the job on time, on budget and to a high standard of quality.

The trades are not composed only of men; some of our best tradespeople have been women. Our plumbers on a recent *This Old House* project, both women, had a challenging job tearing out old plumbing and putting in new plumbing while keeping some of the plumbing "live" because the homeowners had decided to live in the house during the renovation. The quality of their work was first-rate. The pipe joints were neatly soldered and wiped down; the runs of pipe were straight and plumb and looked good even where they are going to be out of sight.

I believe construction is on the verge of change. Labor and material costs will alter how buildings are built. For example, I foresee the use of more modular units and greater emphasis on energy efficiency. Keeping up with building technology will be ever more important. You will have to be an outstanding craftsperson, not just an adequate one, if you want to stay as busy as you'd like.

And if you want to go into business for yourself, you will find that a computer is as important as any tool in your tool chest, because to stay profitable you will have to be able to make quick and accurate bids and to keep close tabs on the cost of your jobs once under way. Also, the neatness and accuracy of bids done on a computer helps you to project an image of honesty, confidence, skill and competence that is critical to your success.

Renovation and construction is a good field, but it is not a cakewalk. You should go into it for the long haul, not with the hope of getting rich quickly. You have to be adaptable and street smart, especially if you want to go into business for yourself.

To be able to work with your hands and to see the product of your hard work standing in three dimensions at the end of a day makes building and renovating a very satisfying career. Construction offers independence and mastery of your own fate. If you work for yourself, you can be your own boss, the master of your own fate, and that offers some security in a world that is increasingly insecure for job seekers. So I say if your dream lies in the construction trades—and you are willing to work hard and work smart—you can live your dream in this field.

SUCCESS STORIES

Joseph Mirlisena Sr., former President, Cincinnati B&J Plumbing Corporation, Pleasant Plain, Ohio

Mirlisena started his career 48 years ago as a plumber's helper to his father. But his fascination with large, fancy and unusual projects lead him to work overhauling the world's largest recirculating swimming pool, a two-acre colossus at Kings Island theme park in Cincinnati, Ohio.

Another favorite job was building the huge fountains there and at Kings Dominion, near Richmond, Virginia. Each has about 80 nozzles and shoots water 30 feet into the air. Asked how he felt when one of these fountains was turned on for the first time, he says, "Elated. To see something no one else has ever done working the way you imagined is a dream come true for a mechanical man like me."

Kevin Awkard, Journeyman Mason, National Park Service, Washington, D.C.

Like most masons, Awkard started out as a laborer. He mixed mortar for journeyman masons, built scaffolds and hauled brick. "You have to learn from the bottom up," his supervisors told him even before he joined an apprenticeship program and went on to work for the National Park Service.

Awkard now works on national monuments and statues, fountains and pools in Washington, D.C. He once had the delicate job of scraping out and replacing mortar between stones of the Washington Monument. The job—all within the interior stair section of the monument—called for carefully analyzing the ingredients of the mortar, which was over 100 years old, and matching them as closely as possible with modern materials. The work was exacting and required the participation of architects and historians. Awkard has done the same for the Jefferson Memorial and has plastered parts of Ford's Theater, where President Lincoln was shot in 1865.

Saws buzz. Hammers whack. Whether carpenters are framing a house, installing French doors or building forms for concrete walls, they are working with a material that feels good beneath their hands. They measure wood, cut it, lay it out in place and hammer, glue or bolt it together to create frames, doors, buildings and more. Their biggest satisfaction: knowing what they build will outlast them.

For years and decades after completing a job, many carpenters will drive by a building, bridge or monument and say, "I helped build that."

Neither rain nor wind nor snow stops most carpenters from doing their work. They work outdoors in all kinds of weather and at all times of year. Hauling wood and other materials and climbing stairs is hard work—and good exercise.

They are the primary builders on any construction site, whether it's a skyscraper, factory, shopping mall, home or even a ship. They shape forms for concrete foundations, construct walls, floors and roofs, install the windows and doors and fasten paneling and ceilings. They're also the craftspeople who do the delicate work of nailing up crown molding and constructing built-in bookcases.

Because carpenters are so involved in a building's construction, they often are promoted to manage the work of people in other trades, such as masons, tile setters, roofers and carpet layers. They may also become estimators (who estimate the cost of a building project for their employers) or building inspectors (who check that the work meets building code regulations for the local government).

Some specialize in an area such as cabinetmaking, concrete form-making or trim work (the woodwork around doors and windows). With experience, many go into business for themselves.

The work can be dangerous, particularly for those employed in commercial construction. Carpenters often walk on single planks hundreds of feet above the ground. The work site is crowded with workers involved in different tasks and operating heavy machinery, such as cranes and pile drivers.

Even though carpenters work with their hands, they must use their minds as well. They read blueprints and specifications and solve complicated problems using their math skills. They figure out how to hang kitchen cabinets straight even when the walls and ceiling of an old house are not straight themselves, and they calculate angle cuts for roof rafters.

If you like seeing the physical results of your labor, using your head as well as your hands and spending a good deal of time outdoors on different work sites, then carpentry may be in your future.

Getting into the Field

What You'll Learn

- ❑ Mastery of arithmetic, especially fractions, and basic geometry
- ❑ How to use hand and power tools safely and precisely
- ❑ How to use rules and measures with accuracy
- ❑ How to read blueprints and envision structures in three dimensions

Necessary Skills

- ❑ Ability to listen well and absorb information
- ❑ Good communication skills

Do You Have What It Takes?

- ❑ Good eye-hand coordination
- ❑ Enjoyment of working with your hands
- ❑ Ability to work as a member of a team
- ❑ Patience and determination
- ❑ Ability to work hard for short periods of time under deadline

Physical Requirements

- ❑ Agility and coordination
- ❑ Ability to climb ladders, maintain good balance on scaffolding
- ❑ Ability to endure harsh weather and loud noises as well as long periods of standing, bending and kneeling

Apprenticeship Program Requirements

- ❑ 18 years old (most programs)
- ❑ At least two years of high school or a diploma or general equivalency diploma (GED)

Licenses Required

None

Job Outlook

Job opportunities will grow: as fast as average

Construction is expected to increase—there will be a demand for new housing, commercial buildings and plants as well as a need to renovate existing structures. Still, jobs are not expected to grow as fast as they have in the past because of the increasing use of prefabricated materials and because new tools make it possible to get more done in less time. Although carpentry jobs exist everywhere, the availability of jobs depends greatly on the condition of the local economy.

The Ground Floor

Entry-level jobs: apprentice, helper

On-the-Job Responsibilities

Beginners

- ❑ Cut lumber
- ❑ Carry construction materials
- ❑ Hold materials while more experienced carpenters fasten them in place
- ❑ Build forms for concrete
- ❑ Frame walls and floors
- ❑ Set window frames
- ❑ Install hardware
- ❑ Attend classes (if you are in a formal apprenticeship program)

Experienced Carpenters

Any of the above, plus:

- ❑ Build wood floors, walls, stairs and roofs from blueprints
- ❑ Use radial arm saws, pneumatic nailers and other commercial tools
- ❑ Calculate complex rafter cuts using framing squares
- ❑ Install cabinets; construct shelves
- ❑ Construct forms for concrete floors and columns
- ❑ Supervise apprentices and other carpenters

When You'll Work

Even though your contract with an employer may call for a 35- or 40-hour workweek, you may be asked to work longer hours—including evenings and weekends—to meet a deadline. Most work begins early. Work is most plentiful in the warm months; layoffs are common in the coldest months. During slow times, carpenters try to do home remodeling jobs.

Time Off

Carpenters often don't work on major holidays, but they are not paid for these or for vacation days, unless otherwise specified in a labor contract. The exception to this rule: carpenters who work for federal or state agencies or for companies that grant such paid days to other employees.

Perks

- ❑ Use of company service vehicles and tools (you're responsible for their safe and timely return)
- ❑ Paid holidays, health insurance and pensions (some union carpenters)

Who's Hiring

- ❑ General contractors (the companies that bid for and oversee entire construction projects)
- ❑ Subcontractors (the companies that perform parts of a job for a general contractor)
- ❑ Home builders
- ❑ Government agencies
- ❑ Maintenance companies
- ❑ Apartment complexes
- ❑ Institutions such as colleges and hospitals
- ❑ Shipyards
- ❑ Manufacturing firms
- ❑ Wholesalers and retailers

On-the-Job Hazards

- ❑ Injuries to hands from hammers, saw blades and splinters
- ❑ Risk of falls from heights and scaffolding
- ❑ Risk of falls because of slippery floors and electrical cords
- ❑ Exposure to possible allergens (for example, wood dust) and hazardous materials (for example, solvents)

Places You'll Go

Beginners and experienced carpenters: Little potential for travel beyond local area

Most carpenters' work is within easy driving distance of their homes. Those in rural areas travel farthest to job sites.

Surroundings

About 60 percent of carpentry work is in residential construction. Consequently, carpenters work outdoors when the job calls for building the shell of a house from basement to roof and indoors after the house is weathertight and the rooms and trim work need finishing. The same is true for commercial and high-rise work.

There's noise and dust and sometimes odors from paint and glue. Carpenters often work alone or with one helper in an isolated room or portion of a building. Carpenters who become cabinetmakers sometimes work in a factory-like indoor setting where machinery noises and dust are plentiful and there are often no windows.

Dollars and Cents

Average hourly union pay: $18

Average hourly non-union pay: $12.50

Time and a half for overtime is common; your hourly rate may be even higher if the work falls on a holiday or Sunday. Union apprentices usually make 40 to 50 percent of a journeyman's wage to start. Most union contracts call for overtime pay after 35 or 40 hours and premium pay for work during unusual hours or on hazardous sites.

Moving Up

In small companies, after you have completed your apprenticeship, you can supervise other carpenters and become the project manager of remodeling and small building projects. In larger companies or agencies, you can be promoted to supervisor or superintendent in charge of a portion of a construction project.

With experience, you can specialize in cabinetmaking, for example, or become a foreman, project manager, estimator or purchasing agent. You can "moonlight" on weekends doing home improvements around the neighborhood. Eventually you can start your own business. When you have a good reputation, word of mouth spreads your name and you can end up with enough work to keep you, and perhaps some helpers, busy full time.

Where the Jobs Are

Jobs for carpenters exist everywhere; job availability mirrors the local economy and real estate market. Generally, in a region where the population is growing, there is a demand for new housing and commercial construction, hence carpentry jobs.

Training

The United Brotherhood of Carpenters and Joiners of America runs an apprenticeship program. Spaces are limited and waiting lists long. Admittance may require passing written and dexterity tests.

The National Association of Home Builders (NAHB), the Associated Builders and Contractors (ABC) and the Associated General Contractors of America (AGC) also run apprenticeship programs. These are similar to the one run by the union, and in fact all four organizations sit on a National Joint Apprenticeship and Training Committee. Find out about NAHB, ABC and AGC programs by calling local chapters or writing the national headquarters.

Trade schools and technical institutes also teach carpentry; so do some correspondence courses. Pre-apprentice programs such as Jobs Corps and programs run under the U.S. Department of Labor's Job Training Partnership Act prepare young people for the union apprentice program or other carpentry certification programs by improving their reading and math skills and giving basic training in carpentry. State governments often run an office of apprenticeship and training.

The Male/Female Equation

More and more women are becoming carpenters, but in 1990 they represented only slightly more than 1 percent of all carpenters. With increasingly sophisticated tools and building materials, strength is needed less and craftsmanship more—a trend that should prove helpful to women.

For more information about women's opportunities in carpentry or any other building careers discussed in this book, write to the National Association of Women in Construction (NAWIC) at 437 South Adams Street, Fort Worth, Texas 76104, or call 800-552-3506.

Making Your Decision: What to Consider

The Bad News

- ❑ Doing "go-fer" and hauling work early on
- ❑ Working outdoors in foul weather
- ❑ Dangerous work conditions on some construction sites
- ❑ A long apprenticeship

The Good News

- ❑ Working outdoors in good weather
- ❑ Ability to make money while you learn
- ❑ Satisfaction of seeing results of your efforts
- ❑ Potential for owning your own business

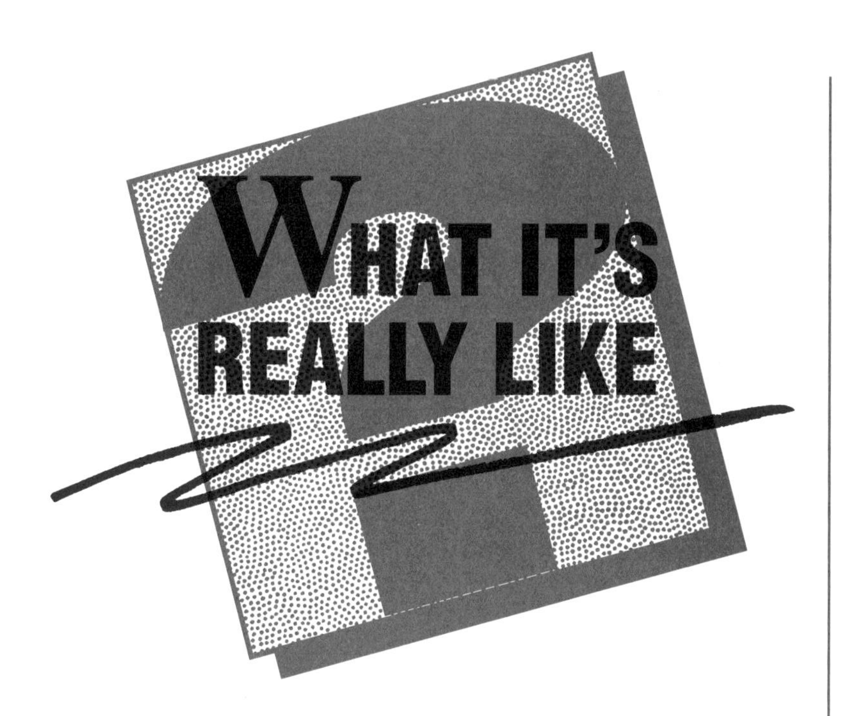

Michael Holland, 29,
residential carpenter,
Yates Construction Company,
Redwood City, California
Years in the field: 11

How did you break into carpentry?
I got my first taste working summers in high school for my brother-in-law. We installed carpets in new homes. I realized I liked seeing buildings being built. After high school a friend told me about an entry-level, part-time job on a home construction site. I swept floors and organized the tools.

Did you join an apprentice program?
No. Nor have I joined the union. After about three months on the home building site, my boss moved me into framing—nailing together the studs for walls and then tilting them into place. I learned from more experienced carpenters, who examined my work and taught me as I went along.

What was it like when you started out?
Typically you're a "go-fer" quite a bit. You go for lumber, tools and even coffee. But it all pays off. You learn about

materials and tools and pick up skills helping older guys.

What do you like about carpentry?
The gauges of your success are very real. You can tell right away if you have done something well or not. You can judge yourself easily, and you can judge others easily by their work. You get to work outside a lot too.

What was the hardest thing about starting out?
Probably the physical labor. As the low man on the job, you end up digging the small ditches that the earth-moving equipment doesn't do; you move lumber piles, and you do foundation framing. You have to have the strength and coordination for the work.

What were some good things about starting out?
Carpentry is one of the quickest ways to higher pay for people just out of high school. And you can take on more responsibility relatively quickly. It took five years for me to start earning a very good wage.

What have you been doing lately?
I work for a company that builds multimillion-dollar homes; it's only my third employer in 11 years. I now have two journeyman carpenters who are good enough to work on their own, so I am the troubleshooter. I have to know what the subcontractors are doing or are about to do and coordinate their work with ours.

What do you like best about your work?
The fact that the decisions you make turn into tangible construction right away and that those decisions will probably be affecting people for a hundred years or more. I like seeing people come on the job site and watching them express amazement at the beauty of the construction.

What do you like least?
Dealing with selfish or nit-picking subcontractors. Some will try to come in, do their work and get out fast without paying enough attention to quality.

What do you feel proudest of?
Getting to the point where I could be the troubleshooter on the job. When I felt that my decisions and my efforts counted as much as anyone's for the survival of this small home-building company, I really felt good.

What advice do you have for those considering the trade?
Take mathematics seriously, especially geometry. Also, you'll be ahead of the game if you are acquainted with the tools.

Tom Cocco, 34,
commercial carpenter,
Fusco Corporation,
Hamden, Connecticut
Years in the field: 13

How did you get interested in carpentry?
When I was in high school, I worked for a cousin who was a jack-of-all-trades. I got interested in carpentry then and applied for the union apprenticeship program.

Did you take a test?
I took a written test and did well enough to become a third-year apprentice.

What was it like at first?
I helped build forms for concrete walls 20 feet high and 14 inches thick. I also had to go for coffee and materials a lot. Basically, you learn by helping the older guys. The more you ask "why?," the more rapidly you learn.

What do you have the hardest time getting used to?
Heights. I'd be up on scaffolding five and six stories high, walking on a single plank.

How many employers have you worked for, and what sort of work have you done?
I've had six employers, the longest for five and a half years. I spent two and a half years building 80 underground tanks for a water treatment plant. I've worked on highways, bridges, a water pumping station and a sports coliseum. I also helped renovate one of the oldest buildings in New Haven, Connecticut.

What do you like best about your work?
Standing back and saying, "I built that." I love working with my hands, and I like working hard and knowing that

not everyone can do what I do. Once we had to make forms for a very large spiral staircase. The staircase had been designed by a computer, but the design wasn't feasible, so we carpenters had to come up with a new way of making it.

What do you like least about your work?
The threat of layoff. When the economy turns down, construction people are often the first to be laid off. Sometimes the travel can be troublesome. For over two years, I worked on a job that was an hour and a half drive away.

What is a job you are particularly proud of?
Once we were building concrete tanks, 80 feet across and 16 feet high. The designers told us we could probably fabricate about ten bays within the tanks a day. We came up with a way of putting together 20 to 30 bays a day. The company was so impressed that they sent a video crew to tape us so other carpenters could see how we had done it.

What advice do you have for someone thinking of going into carpentry?
Shop and blueprint-reading classes are useful; so are classes that can teach you electrical work, plumbing and masonry. Try the work out by taking a summer job. If you're thinking of coming into a union apprenticeship program, you can't come in with a "big head"—you have lots to learn.

Lucy Nehls, 40,
remodeling contractor,
Carpentry by Lucy,
Asheville, North Carolina
Years in the field: 15

How did you break into carpentry?
I lost my job as a fitness instructor and began looking through the *Yellow Pages* for job ideas. I saw "Apprentice Programs" and called up. I had no carpentry background at all; I didn't even know what a drill bit was.

Were you tested?
Yes, for dexterity and knowledge of mathematics. I was accepted into the program and began taking night courses through the local community college even before I got a day carpentry job. I took mathematics, blueprint reading, carpentry and first aid.

Was the apprenticeship program helpful?
Yes. I worked with the Carolinas Construction Training Council, which is affiliated with the U.S. Department of Labor. If you get into carpentry by just joining a company, you can end up doing too much sweeping and digging. At the end of the four-year program, I was given my journeyman's certificate; it's a mark of professionalism that is respected. The program did not require me to join the union.

What was your early work like?
At first, shoveling and sweeping. But gradually I moved to hammering and working with power tools. I was helped along, not thrown into the water and left to sink or swim. We worked on $3 million and $4 million commercial buildings.

Were you spared work because you are a woman?
Absolutely not. I did everything a man in my position did.

Did people make it hard on you because you are a woman?
Some did. Some threw rocks at my car; others put bugs in my food. But I was determined to become skilled. I found out that the more experience I got, the more respect I received.

Other than harassment, what did you find difficult early on?
Getting accustomed to using the tools, some of which seemed awkward to me and made my muscles sore, like turning pliers all day. And I found the weather sometimes difficult to deal with, hammering outside in 14-degree windy weather or working on a roof on a 100-degree day.

How long did it take you to feel established?
About five years. There are really a lot of facets to carpentry, a lot to learn and a lot of experience to gain.

What were your early jobs like?
I worked many years for a general contractor. We built many types of commercial buildings. I did everything from laying them out to building the foundation, erecting the walls and installing the locks. I worked my way from apprentice to carpenter to lead carpenter to supervisor. I also worked for the U.S. Civil Service for two years, remodeling World War II buildings and doing service calls.

What do you do now?
For the last four years, I've run my own residential remodeling business. My partner and I own two trucks and thousands of dollars' worth of tools. Building decks, closets and bookcases and removing interior walls are typical jobs.

Is there a benefit to being a woman business owner in remodeling?
Some women clients say they are more comfortable having us rather than men in their homes; some say we listen better.

What do you like most about carpentry?
Creating. You go in at the beginning of the day, and even in a few hours you can see the work you have done, maybe some built-in bookcases or a pair of beautiful French doors. I also like the challenge of figuring out problems. I also enjoy getting better and better at my craft.

What do you like least?
Heights. You can be in some dangerous situations and have to work around dangerous machinery. I didn't like being two stories high on a steel beam working with a nailing gun.

What are you proudest of?
Going into business for myself. People dream of being their own boss, and I am living that dream.

What advice do you have for someone considering carpentry as a career?
You should have a desire to do it, because it is hard and challenging work. Get a foot in any way you can and join an apprenticeship program. I get calls from people who want me to work for them just because I have a journeyman's card.

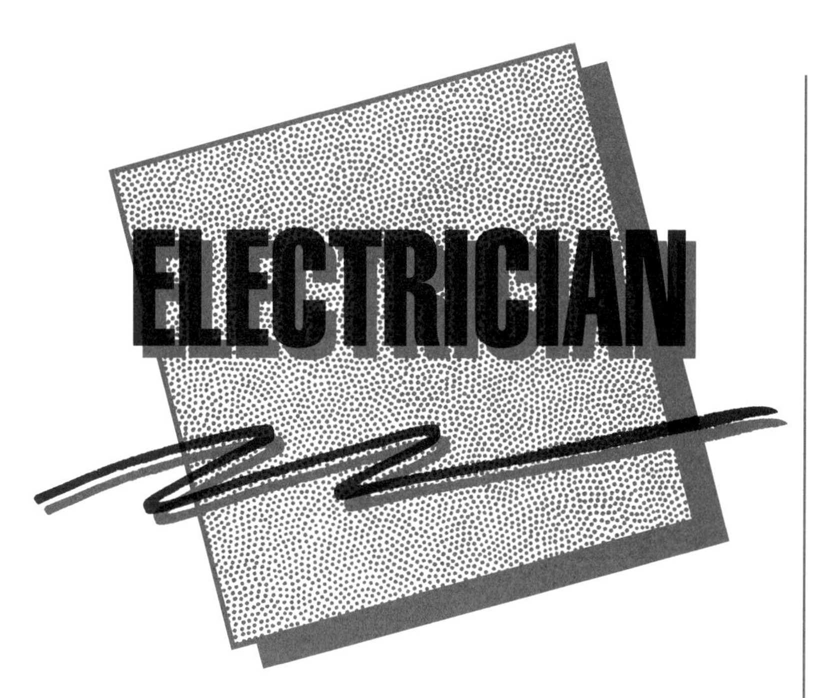

They wriggle through tight crawl spaces. They string cable on high ladders or poles. They are often at new construction sites, pulling cable through unfinished walls and nipping and then connecting small wires that run to control panels. When their work is done, the flick of a switch brings light, heat and sound to once-lifeless buildings and machines. That's the magic electricians make.

Electricians time their work around carpenters, plumbers and other construction site workers. They route power when and where it is needed. Electricians are detectives and troubleshooters, using diagnostic equipment and their skills to unravel problems in circuits or machinery. Many work in construction, wiring new homes, shopping centers and office buildings.

Some work in factories, hospitals or universities, where they maintain equipment or work to improve the controls and instruments of machines and laboratories. Some choose utility work, focusing their efforts on gigantic dynamos, massive transformers, humming power plants or the poles and towers that carry electrical cables.

Electrical work includes a host of subfields such as communications, fiber optics, computer system installation, electric sign work, marine electrical work, broadcasting, railroad work and line work—repairing and installing cables that run from power pole to power pole.

There's more to being an electrician than twisting wires and pulling cable. You have to understand the science of electricity—how it is generated, why it works the way it does—and which equipment and cables can safely handle different electrical loads.

You need to be aware of your safety—and the safety of those you work with—at all times because you will often be working with "live" wires and cables. When you're experienced, you will be able to recite portions of the thick National Electrical Code by heart and read the specialized blueprints and circuit diagrams that are the written language of electrical work. Because of their knowledge and skills, electricians command some of the highest wages and best benefits of any construction workers.

Most electricians learn their trade through four- or five-year apprenticeship programs or by working as an electrician's helper. This trade is a good one for women, since brute strength is not nearly as important as being able to master information about building and safety codes and to perform the exacting work of making connections.

If you have an aptitude for math and science, enjoy problem solving and have the determination to get through a demanding apprenticeship, consider connecting with the electrician trade.

Getting into the Field

What You'll Learn

- ❑ How electricity is generated and how it works
- ❑ Electrical theory as applied to motors, transformers, batteries and machinery
- ❑ Geometry
- ❑ Blueprint reading for electrical layouts
- ❑ How to read circuit diagrams
- ❑ The workings of testing equipment such as ammeters and oscilloscopes

Necessary Skills

- ❑ Knowledge of hand and power tools such as screwdrivers, knives, wire cutters and heavy-duty drills
- ❑ Basic knowledge of carpentry
- ❑ Ability to work with people to get a job done

Do You Have What It Takes?

- ❑ Ability to work carefully (danger is real) and precisely
- ❑ No fear of heights or cramped, dark spaces
- ❑ Attention to detail
- ❑ Willingness to work in all kinds of weather

Physical Requirements

- ❑ Good finger dexterity
- ❑ Good eyesight (and color vision), hearing and sense of smell
- ❑ Good upper-body strength for carrying heavy coils of wire

Apprenticeship Program Requirements

- ❑ 18 years old
- ❑ High school diploma or general equivalency diploma (GED)
- ❑ Good health

Licenses Required

Most areas require electricians to be licensed; licensing requirements vary, but applicants must usually pass an exam that tests their knowledge of basic electricity theory, the National Electrical Code and local electrical and building codes.

Job Outlook

Job openings will grow: faster than average

As the population and economy grow, more electricians will be needed to install and service electrical systems. Openings will vary depending on the health of the construction and manufacturing sectors of the economy in any one region and the number of electricians available there.

The Ground Floor

Entry-level jobs: apprentice, helper

On-the-Job Responsibilities

Beginners

- ❏ Drill holes in wood wall studs and in floor and ceiling joists
- ❏ Pull cable through drilled holes; nail outlet and switch boxes and ceiling fixture boxes to wall and ceiling studs and joists
- ❏ Connect wires in outlet and switch boxes
- ❏ Mount circuit breaker panels on walls, install circuit breakers, connect appliances to circuit cables
- ❏ Bend and join pieces of metal conduit
- ❏ Check circuits with test equipment

Experienced Electricians

Any of the above, plus:

- ❏ Plan and draw diagrams for whole electrical systems
- ❏ Supervise electricians or electrical work on a project

When You'll Work

Even though your contract with an employer may call for a 35- or 40-hour workweek, you may be asked to work longer hours—including evenings and weekends—to meet a deadline. If you work in a factory or as a maintenance electrician in an institution or plant, you may work evening or night shifts.

Time Off

Full-time, permanent employees often get major holidays off and have the same vacation benefits as other employees of the company or as specified in labor contracts. Those who work for contractors may be laid off when a construction project has ended or any time foul weather strikes.

Perks

- ❑ Access to company trucks and tools (some employers)
- ❑ Paid vacation days, health insurance and pensions (some full-time, permanent employees and some union electricians)

Who's Hiring

- ❑ Electrical contractors
- ❑ Manufacturing companies that operate factories
- ❑ Institutions such as hospitals and universities
- ❑ Computer systems installation companies
- ❑ Oil refineries and chemical plants

Places You'll Go

Beginners and experienced electricians: little opportunity for travel

The exception is linemen, who can be sent into remote rural areas to connect high-voltage cables to poles and transmission towers.

Surroundings

Electricians who work at residential and commercial construction sites are exposed to noise and extreme weather. They may have to work in dark crawl spaces. Power plants and utility power substations do not have many people around; you'll keep company with huge dynamos, transformers and high-voltage towers. Factories can be noisy and bustling with moving equipment and people. Lineman work outdoors, often in rural or wilderness areas.

On-the-Job Hazards

- ❑ Shocks, which can be fatal
- ❑ Falls from ladders, towers and poles
- ❑ Cuts and nicks to the hands and fingers
- ❑ Exposure to some toxic chemicals such as PCBs, a carcinogen used in old transformers

Dollars and Cents

Average hourly pay for union journeyman: $19

Average hourly pay for non-union journeyman: $8-$13.50

Time and a half for overtime is common; your hourly rate may be even higher if the work falls on a holiday or a Sunday. Apprentices typically earn 40 to 50 percent of a journeyman's wage and reach 90 percent of that rate about six months prior to completing their program.

Moving Up

Some journeymen specialize in a particular area such as machinery control, utility work, instrumentation or telecommunications. Many journeyman electricians eventually move up to foreman and may be in charge of 10 to 15 other journeymen. A few get promoted to superintendent in charge of a large project. An electrician can also move into the office of an electrical contractor and be an estimator, going to job sites and helping to work on the bids that win jobs for the employer. In addition, thousands of journeymen have gone into business for themselves as small electrical contractors.

Where the Jobs Are

Electricians are most in demand where commercial and residential construction is strong and where power plants and factories are located.

Training

Four- and five-year apprenticeship programs are run by a joint training committee of the International Brotherhood of Electrical Workers and local chapters of the National Electrical Contractors Association. They are also available through local electrical contracting companies in conjunction with local chapters of the Associated Builders and Contractors and Independent Electrical Contractors.

A typical apprenticeship program calls for 144 hours of class study plus 8,000 hours of on-the-job training and qualifies you for both construction and maintenance electrical work.

The Male/Female Equation

In 1990, women made up almost 2 percent of all electricians—the highest percentage of any of the trades featured in this book.

Making Your Decision: What to Consider

The Bad News

- ❑ Working with potentially fatal voltages
- ❑ Less control over a project than other tradespeople have
- ❑ Rigorous apprenticeship (particularly learning codes)

The Good News

- ❑ Highest pay among construction workers
- ❑ "Clean" work
- ❑ Lowest unemployment rate among construction workers

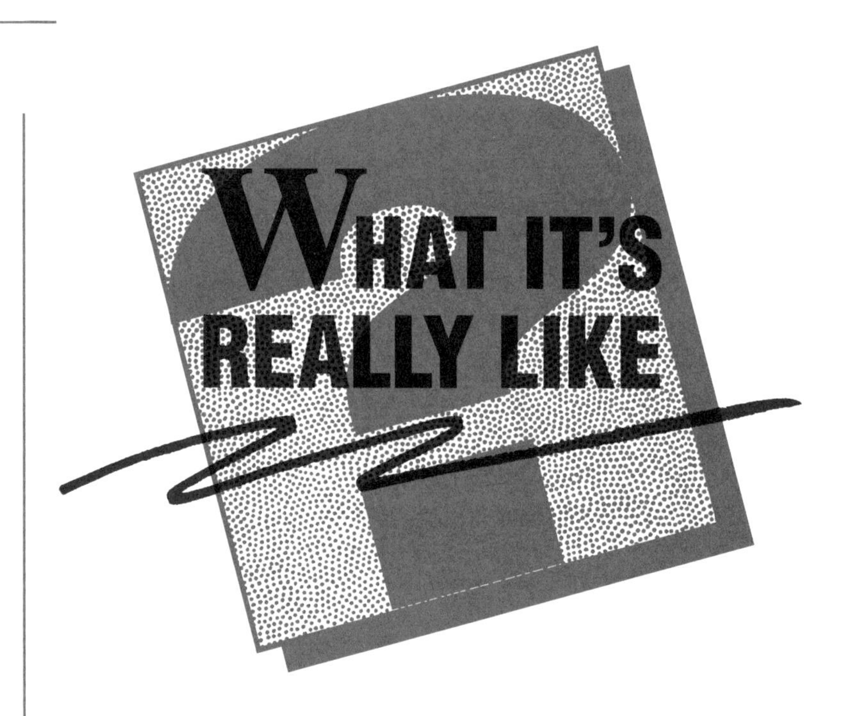

Richard Kuniski, 28,
journeyman lineman,
Sturgen Electric Corporation,
Phoenix, Arizona
Years in the field: four

How did you get started in lineman work?
Some friends who worked for an electric utility company told me that the company needed help for the summer. I got hired and liked the work enough to continue.

What sort of work were you doing?
Ground work. When you're not a journeyman or apprentice, you can't climb the poles or work in the buckets (that extend from booms on electric company trucks). So I did things like drill holes for the power poles and holes for the anchors that hold some of the poles up. I did this work for ten months and decided I wanted to be a journeyman lineman, so I applied to the union apprenticeship program.

Was getting in difficult?
No. I took an aptitude test that had rather simple math on it. I also had an oral interview with the local committee. I signed on to a four-year program, which I recently finished, and recently passed my journeyman's test.

What did being an apprentice involve?
Besides working our regular jobs, helping the journeyman linemen set up power poles and fix high-voltage wires, we'd be in class one Saturday a month for eight hours. The first year we learned how to climb poles. The second year was a lot more about electrical theory. We learned how to hook up transformers on poles and how to safely touch and move high-voltage wire with fiberglass sticks.

What kind of work do you do now?
The company I work for bids on jobs for the utility company here. We put in new poles and run new high-voltage wires or move old poles. The poles might be 35 to 100 feet high. Mostly we work out of buckets, two linemen to a bucket, the second beside the first to make sure you don't get too close to touching something you shouldn't. The high-voltage wires are usually live. The bucket is insulated, so in theory you can touch a live wire and not be shocked, but you still have to put safety first. I've never been shocked or had a fall.

What kinds of things do you do when the wires are live?
We'll change transformers, insulators and fuses. We'll take out and put in new cross arms that hold the wires.

What sort of gear do you wear?
Always a hard hat, long sleeves even in summer and safety glasses.

Do you find the work physically difficult?
It can be. I'm jumping in and out of a truck a lot and lifting things out of or into a truck. I have to lift manhole covers, and they can be pretty heavy.

Have you traveled much?
Yes. When work was slow here, I found work in Kansas, Iowa and Idaho. My wife came with me. The longest we were away from Phoenix was about three months. We put up high-voltage transmission towers and installed the wire on them. This can be heavy work; the wires are thicker and everything's bulkier, but I like it. We'd cross rivers and mountains. We were always outdoors in rural areas.

Does the weather ever bother you?
Sometimes. In Phoenix, summer temperatures reach well

over 100 degrees. We work harder in the mornings and slow down a bit in the hot afternoons. We drink lots of water too.

Do you find a lot of variety in your work?
Yes. My company installs substations and underground lines. I've installed fiber optic cable; it's strung into a part of the high-voltage cable.

What do you like most about your job?
The challenge of it. You keep having to figure things out. It's a good trade, especially if you like the outdoors.

Have you ever been laid off?
Yes, when I first started, but not since then. The demand for linemen is supposed to be very high over the next ten years.

What advice would you have for someone considering becoming a lineman?
You should study math, especially algebra. I use it, for example, when I have to calculate how much cable I need to anchor a pole. Make sure it's what you want to do.

Mark Gamble, 31, journeyman inside wireman, Juneman Electric Company, Birmingham, Alabama Years in the field: six

How did you get into the electrical trade?
My father-in-law was an electrician, and he told me how to apply to an apprenticeship program. I took an aptitude test and a test to see how much I already knew about math and electricity. I also had a personal interview with the apprenticeship program committee. Several months later I got in and was directed to an employer for whom I worked for about a year. Over the five years of the apprenticeship, I worked for seven employers so I could learn different skills.

What did you do in the beginning?
For the first few months, I got familiar with the tools and materials. Then they put me with a journeyman wireman in a power plant. We installed conduit (pipes into which cable is fed) and pulled wire to a motor control center. I helped route the wire in place, but as a first-year apprentice, I was not allowed to make the wire connections. I was taking orders from journeymen who were younger than me, but I knew they had paid their dues and knew more than I did.

What was the classroom work like?
We met Monday nights from 5:30 to 9:30. In the first year we learned the basics of electricity plus Ohm's Law and other formulas electricians use. In the second year we learned about motor control, hookups and more, but most hands-on work was done on the job.

Did you find the classes difficult?
Not particularly. But it got harder as you went along, and you had to stay on top of it. In the fifth year we were learning program logic control, which gets pretty complicated.

Were you tested on what you knew?
Each year we had 12 tests, plus a semester test and a year-end test. At the very end of the apprenticeship program, we took the Florida Block Test, which tests your knowledge of the National Electrical Code. I think you need to be in a program to gain the knowledge needed to pass.

How dangerous is your work?
You have to constantly worry about safety. Sometimes you're climbing high, and you really have to watch yourself. But you can also get hurt from "simple" accidents: I stepped off a six-foot ladder the wrong way and tore some knee cartilage during my first year. I had surgery and missed work for several days.

What's involved in wiring a house?
A lot of it is pulling wire. You also hook up switches and receptacles, and you have to wire the main circuit-breaker panel. It's mostly clean work. But doing electrical work in an existing house can get tricky and dirty. You have to run wire behind existing walls. You run into cross braces, and it gets frustrating at times. It's a lot harder than wiring new houses.

What do you like most about your work?
Being able to set my own pace. The supervisors tell you what has to be done, and then you just do it without anyone looking over your shoulder. It's also very satisfying to see a job through from the beginning to the end. I like that better than starting one aspect of a job and having someone else finish it. And I like learning something new every day.

What do you like least?
The dirt and the danger. You can get hurt in a split second, so you have to be on your toes.

What advice would you give to someone thinking about becoming an electrician?
It's a great field of work. If you are young and single, you can have good income, and with your journeyman's card you can travel a lot too.

Patricia Brown, 48,
journeyman electrician,
Sasco Electric,
Denver, Colorado
Years in the field: seven

How did you get into electrical work?
I was always interested in electrical systems, but there were few opportunities for women to enter the trade. After years of working as a cashier and at clerical jobs, I applied to an apprenticeship program. I waited 18 months for an opening. My first job was with a company doing commercial work. I went to classes two nights a week in the union hall.

What sorts of things did you learn?
Electrical theory, how to install conduit, how to bend the conduit and how to install electrical panels, switches, receptacles and lighting.

Has it been difficult being a woman in this trade?
It wasn't easy. Women don't always get the skill training that is useful in this trade. I had to relearn geometry and

trigonometry. But the male journeymen were helpful, and some of them really went out of their way for me. By my third or fourth year, most men realized that I was willing to learn and pull my own weight, and they respect that. Occasionally, I'll run across a man who simply doesn't want to work with a woman.

Was the journeyman's test difficult?
Yes. It was a five-hour test that covered everything I'd been taught over the previous four years. Those who were not conscientious during the apprenticeship program might have to take it two or three times before they pass.

What kind of work have you been doing lately?
I generally work in office buildings. In new buildings I install conduit and electrical panels. I put in the boxes for plugs, switches and fluorescent lighting. I work in all rooms of new construction. I have to read blueprints. The work site is often noisy, but it's generally clean work.

Have you ever been injured?
I was shocked once, but that was because someone did not cap off a wire properly; the power was supposed to be off and it wasn't. Fortunately, it didn't really hurt me.

What do you like most about your work?
Before I became an apprentice, I had great respect for anyone who could go in and know what makes a light go on, and now I can do it. I particularly like the satisfaction of covering up the walls and having the whole system work like it should.

Do you use your arm muscles much to bend the conduit?
For the small conduit, you use a hand tool that requires some muscle, but for the larger conduit, you use a power machine.

What advice would you give someone considering this trade?
You can try a pre-apprenticeship program of up to a year of working with a contractor to see if this is really what you want to do. If you have a good head for figures, I think it's a wonderful profession. The more math courses you can take, the better off you are going to be.

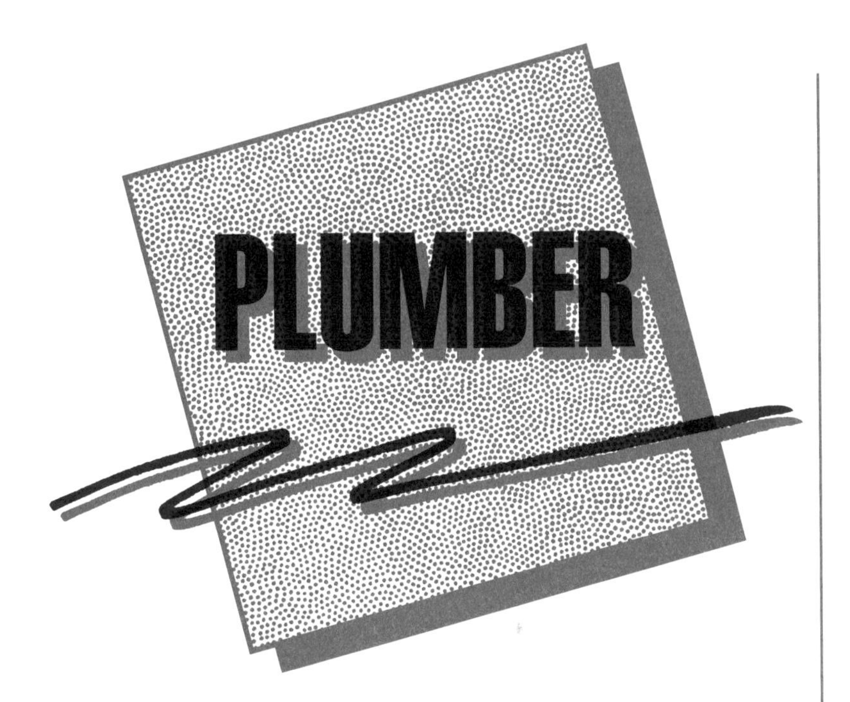

A sheet metal worker has relocated an overhead heating duct. Your mission: to figure out how to reroute the fire sprinkler pipes *quickly* so that other construction workers are not idled. You take measurements, figure angles and apply formulas, making sure the new solution meets local and national safety codes. Then you cut and install the pipe so construction can continue.

Plumbers and their kindred tradesmen, pipefitters, are the masters of hydraulics—the technology of anything that flows in the form of liquid or gas. Whatever is routed through pipes—petroleum, steam, natural gas, chemicals, soda pop, soup and a thousand other substances—reaches its destination thanks to plumbers and pipefitters.

Residential plumbers—with whom most of us are familiar—make house calls to fix clogged drains, repair pipe joints, thaw frozen pipes and install bathroom and kitchen fixtures and water heaters. They do work on the radiator heating system, too, if the house has one.

They also can be found on home construction sites—installing the new water supply pipes and wastewater systems. They're essential to kitchen and bathroom remodeling jobs.

Homeowners sometimes gripe about how much plumbers charge. But there's a simple reason for their high fees: Each journeyman plumber is a highly trained professional and has worked through a four- to five-year apprenticeship while studying the physics of liquids and gases, mechanical drawing, geometry and welding. To gain a master's license and go into business for themselves, plumbers have to study more and pass more tests. About one in six plumbers is self-employed.

To be successful as a plumber, you have to be a good problem solver. Routing pipes can be tricky, since you are likely to be confronted with wooden studs and joists, wide heating ducts, electrical lines and sometimes concrete walls or old, immovable cast iron pipes. Plumbers have to figure out how to make their pipes run, jog and dodge each obstruction, slope at the proper degree if they are waste pipes, not bend too sharply if they are supply pipes and vent through the roof close enough to toilets or sinks to conform to the local plumbing codes.

Commercial plumbers install the vast piping systems for chemical and petroleum plants, put in fire sprinkler systems in shopping centers, install pumps in skyscrapers and more. They work at rocket launching sites and electric generating plants, in ships and on airplanes. Pipefitters generally work for municipalities or government agencies installing water lines, sewer systems and water and wastewater treatment plants.

If you like working with tools, have a good head for math and like the idea of solving problems, read on to find out more about how you can become a plumber.

Getting into the Field

What You'll Learn

- ❑ Basic mathematics skills (geometry and trigonometry)
- ❑ The properties of copper, plastic, steel and brass and how to cut, bend and join them
- ❑ National and local sanitary, plumbing and building codes
- ❑ Knowledge of gases and pressures, gaskets and valves

Necessary Skills

- ❑ How to use hand and power tools
- ❑ Safety consciousness; ability to follow procedures
- ❑ Ability to get along with many types of homeowners (residential plumbers)
- ❑ Willingness to sell products (residential plumbers)

Do You Have What It Takes?

- ❑ Mechanical aptitude
- ❑ Interest in solving unexpected problems

Physical Requirements

- ❑ Better-than-average upper-body strength and a strong back
- ❑ No phobias about heights or confined spaces
- ❑ Good finger dexterity (ability to work with small parts)
- ❑ Willingness to work in all kinds of weather
- ❑ Stamina to work on your feet most of the day

Apprenticeship Program Requirements

- ❑ 18 years old
- ❑ High school diploma or general equivalency diploma (GED)
- ❑ Good health

Licenses Required

Most communities require plumbers to be licensed, which usually involves passing an exam on trade and local plumbing codes. Some states require a separate license for those working on natural gas piping. Plumbers going into business must usually earn a master plumber's license.

Job Outlook

Job openings will grow: about as fast as average

Because the U.S. population is expanding, more buildings—commercial and residential—will need servicing or construction. Jobs with maintenance contractors (who are hired by large employers) are expected to increase more quickly.

The Ground Floor

Entry-level jobs: apprentice, helper

On-the-Job Responsibilities

Beginners

- ❑ Gather pipes and fittings for the next day's work
- ❑ Keep track of inventory and tools
- ❑ Cut holes in framing studs and joists
- ❑ Cut pipe
- ❑ Help with soldering and welding
- ❑ Help install sinks, water heaters, toilets and pipe
- ❑ Unclog drains

Experienced Plumbers

Any of the above, plus:

- ❑ Estimate what materials are needed on a job (and their cost)
- ❑ Figure out angles and lengths of pipe needed for a repair or installation
- ❑ Supervise a kitchen and bath remodeling crew

When You'll Work

Even though your contract with an employer may call for a 35- or 40-hour workweek, you may be asked to work longer hours—including evenings and weekends—to meet a deadline. Most plumbers take their turn being "on call" for emergencies, which can occur anytime. Plumbers and pipefitters who work for petroleum, chemical or other industrial plants sometimes work evening and night shifts.

Time Off

Union plumbers get holidays off as stipulated in their union contract or agreement with the employer. Plumbers working on projects sensitive to weather conditions, such as raising new buildings from scratch, may be idled when the weather is bad, and plumbers tied to the real estate market, such as those who install plumbing in new tract houses, can be idled when new construction slows.

Perks

- ❑ Use of a company truck and company tools
- ❑ Access to a tool shop
- ❑ Health care insurance and paid vacation (some employers)

Who's Hiring

- ❑ Plumbing contractors
- ❑ Mechanical contractors
- ❑ Plumbing maintenance contractors
- ❑ Large factories, plants and government facilities with a great deal of piping

Places You'll Go

Beginners and experienced plumbers: Potential for travel highest for employees of mechanical contractors

Those who work for a mechanical contractor may be asked to go anywhere in the country, even overseas, if an employer wins a contract there.

Surroundings

Residential plumbers who do service work usually work indoors and must often wriggle through dirty, damp crawl spaces or work in basements. Those employed by contractors work inside and outside at residential construction sites, where the noise and dust level can be high.

Plumbers employed by mechanical contractors often work in high-rise buildings or other commercial buildings or factories. Noise levels can be intense.

On-the-Job Hazards

- ❑ Cuts and scrapes from cutting tools
- ❑ Burns from propane torches and steam lines
- ❑ Falls from ladders and scaffolding
- ❑ Possibility of exposure to toxic substances

Dollars and Cents

Average hourly union pay: $20
Average hourly non-union pay: $13

Time and a half for overtime is common; your hourly rate may be even higher if the work falls on a holiday or a Sunday. Apprentices are generally paid about half of a journeyman's wage to begin and receive raises every six months until they are making about 90 percent of a journeyman's wage near the end of the apprentice program.

Moving Up

After a year or more working as a journeyman (a master plumber's license helps, too), a plumber who has demonstrated skills in training and working with others as well as additional management skills may be tapped to become a supervisor or foreman. A field supervisor visits work sites and oversees the work of journeymen and apprentices. A shop supervisor stays in the office and handles the paperwork for field jobs. An estimate supervisor figures out the type and size of equipment needed for jobs and helps to prepare bids.

With a master plumber's license, you also have the option of going into business for yourself. About three-fourths of the mechanical contractors running their own businesses today were once apprentice plumbers.

Where the Jobs Are

The number of jobs in any location mirrors the population. The presence of oil refineries, chemical plants and nuclear power plants increases the number of jobs in an area. Because much new construction is in suburban areas (particularly the Sunbelt states), more new construction jobs can be found there. In inner cities, repair and replacement of plumbing systems represents much of the work; plumbers also work on water distribution and sewer systems projects.

Training

Virtually all plumbers and pipefitters undergo an apprenticeship lasting four to five years—the longer period is for the union apprenticeship program. These programs are run by the United Association of Journeymen and Apprentices of the Plumbing and Pipefitting Industry of the United States and Canada (commonly referred to as the UA), the Mechanical Contractors Association of America, the National Association of Plumbing-Heating-Cooling Contractors and the National Fire Sprinkler Association.

Non-union apprenticeship programs are run by the Associated Builders and Contractors of America, the National Association of Plumbing-Heating-Cooling Contractors and the National Association of Home Builders Institute. You can, however, apply for union membership after becoming a journeyman.

Apprentices put in a regular workweek and attend classes two nights a week—about 216 hours of in-class time each year. Armed Forces training in plumbing and pipefitting is considered good preparation and translates into credit in the apprenticeship program.

The Male/Female Equation

In 1990, women represented less than 1 percent of the trade. Apprenticeship programs are making efforts to reach out to more women.

Making Your Decision: What to Consider

The Bad News

- ❑ A long apprenticeship
- ❑ Occasional emergency "on call" work
- ❑ Work can be dirty and dangerous

The Good News

- ❑ Better than average pay in the construction field
- ❑ Opportunity to go into business for yourself
- ❑ Chance to switch area of specialization

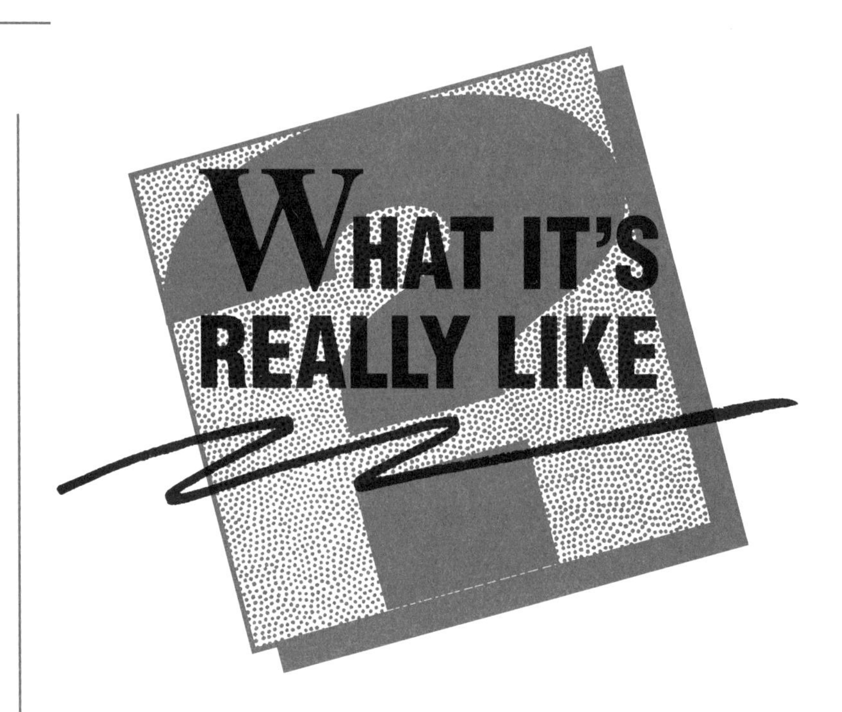

Charles Roseburrough, 27,
pipefitter,
Rand & Son Construction Company,
Kansas City, Missouri
Years in the field: six

How did you get into pipefitting?
I worked for an uncle who did remodeling. It was okay right after high school, but I wanted to have a real trade. So I applied for a union apprentice program in pipefitting. I was accepted and got an interview with a contracting company, which hired me. I recently completed my five-year apprenticeship and have been a journeyman for one year.

What was work like in the beginning?
As they say in the trade, "you work a lot of wrenches," which means you tighten a lot of joints. You also do a lot of lifting and carry pipe. You build a lot of upper-body strength; I went from a size 40 jacket to size 48 in four years.

What were the classes like?
They ran from September to May. The first year is an introduction to tools and the trade, basic math, welding and soldering copper. In the second year, we learned science, heat-

ing systems and boilers. In the third year, it's refrigeration. In the fourth, it's blueprint reading, mechanical drawing and electives for the specialty you've chosen.

What was the hardest part at first?
Lifting the heavy equipment and pipe. Also, I didn't like the height work; we had to walk on steel girders a lot. But it's like anything else—the more you do it, the easier it gets.

What do you currently do?
We've been going into chemical and pharmaceutical plants with enormous runs of pipe. Generally, we go into existing plants and rip out old pipe, then put in new stainless steel piping because it is part of a sterile system. Often that calls for special welding. Sometimes there are odors—and noise that requires earplugs. We wear safety glasses and hard hats.

Is there variety in your work?
Yes. I now go from place to place doing different things. I weld joints, set the pipe in place for others to join, cut threads for pipe joints and connect pipe with couplings. I might be working with fiberglass, plastic or steel pipe.

What have you liked most about your work?
The sense of accomplishment. The fact that I can look back at what I have done and be able to say, "I did that, and I did it right."

What do you like least?
Noise, smells and the often rigorous nature of the work. Some days you do light work, but you make up for that on the days you do really physical work.

What advice would you have for people thinking of becoming pipefitters?
The money and the benefits are good. And you are treated better than many construction people, who are denied overtime and health benefits and who feel they have to have two jobs to earn enough money. With a trade, no one will ever be able to take what you know away from you.

Dave Gallagher, 25,
commercial plumber,
Joseph Stong, Inc.,
Chester, Pennsylvania
Years in the field: eight

How did you get interested in plumbing?
Since I was 12, I have liked working with my hands. I worked for a neighbor who had his own plumbing business during summers since I was 14. I really loved the work.

How did you join an apprenticeship program?
After high school I went to the Master Plumbers' Association. It runs a non-union apprenticeship program here. They took applicants like me who had a full-time job with a master plumber who was one of their members.

What was your classroom work like?
I went to class two nights a week for 28 weeks a year. Each year of the five-year program we studied something different. In the first year it was basic plumbing; in the second it was math—mostly algebra—and basic wiring that you would need to fix boilers. The third year it was drafting and blueprint reading; the fourth was shop work; and the fifth was business.

How long have you been with your present employer?
By the second year of the program, I decided that I wanted to move out of residential work and get into commercial work. I went to work with my present company, a mechanical contractor, and I have been with it for seven years.

What kinds of work do you do?
We do the plumbing for things like office buildings, medical buildings, hotels, nursing homes and industrial parks. We arrive very early on and set pipe in the foundations, then work the pipe up as the walls are erected. In this stage, we're out in the weather all the time. We rough in bathrooms and kitchens and set boilers. We'll work with plastic pipe, copper and cast iron and join them in different ways, too, depending on the local code. Once the interior walls have been completed, we come back to install the toilets, showers, sinks and so on.

I've also replaced boilers in apartment buildings—sometimes working 24 hours straight because no one likes to be without heat or hot water. And I've worked in factories, putting in pipe for new machinery, compressed air or natural gas.

What sort of safety equipment do you wear?
Always safety glasses, sometimes a hard hat, depending on the job. Sometimes when we do soldering we wear long sleeves.

What kinds of dangers do you have to be aware of?
Solvents can be a problem. You should always know what you are using. And when working on old pipe, you should know what used to be flowing in it; we sometimes have to wear respirators because of chemicals that used to be in the pipes.

Have you traveled much?
Some. Our company does a lot of service work for a large corporation. We've had to service one of their plants in northern New Jersey, so we'd go up there and work for a week at a time, then come back.

What do you like most about your work?
I find it very rewarding. I can see physical progress. I like to see a building rise out of a place that was once only a field. I like going out to a job site the day before the work is to begin and writing up a materials list, and then, as the job goes on, figuring out how close I was in estimating how much of everything was needed. I make good money, and I'm building a new house. I've never been laid off.

What do you like least?
Getting a call on my emergency beeper to go out on service work when my working day is over. That can be tough.

Do plumbers get respect on the job site?
Definitely. For one, a lot of other workers believe we make the best money. We also feel there's going to be good demand for us in the years ahead.

What advice would you give someone considering this trade?
Take math. Also, get a job with a small residential plumb-

ing company. You'll learn about how a basic house plumbing system works. If you think you want to be a commercial plumber, it's best to start out in residential because you learn lots of practical skills. If you begin on the big commercial jobs, you never really get a feel for how the whole system works.

Don Pierson, 29,
residential plumber,
Long's Corporation,
Fairfax, Virginia
Years in the field: 13

Describe your early work and learning experiences.
I did not attend college. I was working in landscaping, but the company went bankrupt. My brother was a plumber and got me a job as a helper, something I did for about two years. I decided I wanted to pursue plumbing as a career. I was not licensed, but I knew enough to go out on my own to fix things.

Were you ever in an apprenticeship program?
No. After four years on the job, however, I was eligible to take the state journeyman plumber's test.

How did you prepare for it?
I took a prep course taught by a plumbing inspector. I went two nights a week for three hours over ten weeks. We went over the whole plumbing code book, what you could and couldn't do in certain situations. He also gave a sample test. Your math has to be good enough to figure the lengths of pipe you'll need and the flow rates of water. The first time, I failed the test. I let a year go by, took the prep course again and passed.

What is residential plumbing work like?
The majority is service calls in existing houses. We fix toilets, repair sewer lines and put in new plumbing for kitchen and bath remodeling.

Is there much heavy work?
There can be. We'll lift four-inch cast iron pipe; each piece

weighs about 80 pounds. But if all you're doing is service work, it's not particularly strenuous.

How important are people skills?
Very. If you don't like working with strangers, you should stick with new construction, and then all you have deal with are supervisors. But when you have to deal with homeowners, you have to know how to work with them. My employer has consultants teach us those skills as well as sales skills so we can sell them on new products.

Do you ever have problems working with homeowners?
Ninety-nine percent of them are fine. But one in a hundred is a problem. One guy used a stopwatch to check if I had worked more than 30 minutes at his house—we bill in 15-minute increments.

What is new construction work like?
I'm often given unusual problems in getting pipe to the proper place without breaking any of the code standards. It's challenging to make it legal and have it look good too.

What do you like most about your work?
I like wrestling with problems, either in new or service work. I like having to come up with a solution and getting a pat on the back from an inspector. I also like working with this company.

What do you like least about residential plumbing work?
The long hours. All of us take turns carrying a pager to answer emergency calls that could come in at any time. You never know when you're through with work or when you might be called in the middle of the night. I also don't care for cleaning drains; it's messy, and you have to haul around a heavy machine.

What advice would you give someone considering this career?
You can make good money. Soon I'll try to get my master's license, and if I pass, I'll be able to go into business for myself and hire my own plumbers. You can go far in this trade. It has challenges and definite rewards.

How does your work compare with the work for your uncle's remodeling company?
The big difference is that as union people we go to a job and take the time to do it right. There's not as much pressure to get the job done fast at the expense of quality. That's one of the values of the apprenticeship program; they teach you how to do the job the right way the first time. I'm not working nights and weekends and dawn to dusk; I'm working regular hours and getting paid better.

The job is a big one: a new brick church. You lay the foundation, then build up the walls. Higher and higher you go, red brick by red brick, fashioning the arched openings for doors and stained glass windows. The scaffolding comes down. Where there was once an empty lot now stands a structure that will exist for generations. And *you* helped build it.

Masonry is probably the oldest building trade; masons built the Pyramids, the Parthenon, the Roman Coliseum, Notre Dame, our nation's Capitol and the Empire State Building, to name a few. What they build lasts.

Laying bricks is a big part of a mason's job. There is a rhythm to the work: picking up the brick, setting it in mortar, tapping it down with a trowel handle and scraping away excess mortar that you then set on top of that brick for the next row.

While bricklaying can be repetitious, there is an art to this craft, particularly when you are laying brick in patterns with such names as Flemish bond, English cross, herringbone and basketweave. There is even variety in the mortar joints between the bricks of a wall; they can be rounded, concave, V-shaped or flush with the brick surface. Each is sculpted with tools called jointers.

Masonry is much more than laying bricks, however. Masons can lay concrete block or cinder block, cover bathroom walls and floors with tile and make patios of terrazzo (concrete with the upper surface washed away to expose marble pebbles). They also build highways, sidewalks and parking garages of concrete and apply the stone veneer to skyscrapers. They lay marble on the floors of fancy hotels and office buildings.

Some masons specialize in a particular kind of work. Cement masons work mainly with concrete. Their work might involve repairing a curb along a suburban street or building concrete columns for a towering office building.

Tile setters lay tile on floors, around bathtubs and showers and above kitchen countertops. They might lay flagstone for a sidewalk or a patio or marble in a vestibule. They lay squared cobblestones for a beautiful driveway or set stone statues on pedestals in a garden.

Most masons learn on the job, starting as helpers to experienced masons. They learn informally as they perform routine tasks for the more experienced craftsmen. Some also take vocational training courses to supplement their on-the-job learning.

Many people enjoy the physical tasks that are the work of masons. British statesman Winston Churchill used to relax by building brick walls in his spare time. Laying tiles, stones or other material is a great hobby but an even better trade if the idea of doing exacting, often artistic, work appeals to you.

Getting into the Field

What You'll Learn

- ❑ Math, especially geometry
- ❑ Chemistry and strengths of types of mortar, brick, cement, concrete, cinder block and more
- ❑ Different brick patterns for wall making

Necessary Skills

- ❑ How to use hand tools such as levels, trowels, rubber mallets, chisels, leveling lines and transits
- ❑ Ability to work with electric tools such as power mixers and power saws that cut brick, stone and tile
- ❑ Ability to handle bricks, cinder blocks and stones with relative ease

Do You Have What It Takes?

- ❑ Willingness to do hard physical labor
- ❑ Willingness to work outdoors in temperature extremes
- ❑ Ability to be exacting and neat in your work

Physical Requirements

- ❑ Better-than-average strength for lifting
- ❑ Stamina to work all day on your feet with much lifting, kneeling and bending
- ❑ A good eye for what's level and plumb (straight up and down)

Apprenticeship Program Requirements

- ❑ 17 years old
- ❑ High school diploma or general equivalency diploma (GED)
- ❑ Good health and physical condition

Licenses Required

Some communities require masons to have a license to build chimneys. You may need to be certified in safety procedures to work on special jobs or in locations such as chemical plants.

Job Outlook

Job openings will grow: about as fast as average

As with most construction jobs, work for masons swells and declines with local economies, real estate fortunes and building trends. Brick facades, marble floors, patios, fireplaces and stone facades on buildings never seem to go out of fashion. Work in industrial kilns and blast furnaces will rise and fall with the fortunes of the basic metals industries.

The Ground Floor

Entry-level jobs: apprentice, laborer, hod carrier, helper

On-the-Job Responsibilities

Beginners

- ❑ Mix mortar
- ❑ Carry bricks, stone and cinder block, often up ladders
- ❑ Erect scaffolding
- ❑ Dig ditches and holes for foundations
- ❑ Lay courses of brick between corners
- ❑ Spread grout between tiles (tile setters)
- ❑ Learn to work with stone and concrete

Experienced Masons

May do any of the above, plus:

- ❑ Set up the corner "leads" of buildings
- ❑ Build window arches and other types of curved openings
- ❑ Build fireplaces and chimneys
- ❑ Supervise or train apprentices
- ❑ Work as a job foreman
- ❑ Set marble and other decorative stone

When You'll Work

Even though your contract with an employer may call for a 35- or 40-hour workweek, you may be asked to work longer hours—including evenings and weekends—to meet a deadline. In hot climates such as the Southwest, you may begin as early as 6 A.M. Those who moonlight work evenings and weekends.

Time Off

Many masons choose to take vacations in winter because that's when business is slowest in most of the country.

Perks

- Off-hours access to tools and company trucks (some employers)
- Health care insurance and paid vacation (some employers)

Who's Hiring

- Masonry contractors
- Tile contractors and stone contractors
- General contractors
- Government agencies, especially highway departments

Places You'll Go

Beginners and experienced masons: little potential for travel

Surroundings

Masons generally work outdoors, creating the foundations and walls for buildings. Work is, however, usually postponed during extreme cold or driving rain. Construction sites are generally muddy, with large trucks and earth-moving equipment coming and going. The sites are often noisy and sometimes bustling as foremen shout orders and workers deliver materials.

Tile setters often work exclusively in bathroooms and kitchens. Terrazzo workers may work in commercial buildings and high rises or outside on patios. Cement masons work outside (doing highways and sidewalks) or on construction sites in the early stages of construction, under the same conditions as masons.

On-the-Job Hazards

- ❑ Scrapes to the hands from trowels and chisels
- ❑ Chapped hands from mortar mix
- ❑ Falls from scaffolds
- ❑ "Cement poisoning," an allergic reaction to the ingredients of cement
- ❑ Respiratory problems from mortar dust and from power saws cutting into brick or stone

Dollars and Cents

Average hourly pay for union journeymen: $14-$25

Average hourly pay for non-union journeymen: $9-$18

Time and a half for overtime is common; your hourly rate may be even higher if the work falls on a holiday or a Sunday. Apprentices begin by making 40 to 50 percent of journeymen's pay. Moonlighting often pays more per hour than regular jobs.

Moving Up

After four or five years as a journeyman, a mason may be asked to work as a layout man, a person who uses the blueprints of a building to locate the lowest courses of the walls. The layout man may or may not be paid more than journeymen—depending on the employer—but has to be expert with blueprints.

After eight or ten years of journeyman experience, a mason might become a foreman and be paid anywhere from 50 cents to $4 an hour more than regular journeymen. A foreman will have half a dozen to several dozen masons working for him. In large jobs, where there might be 40 or more masons, the employer will raise someone to superintendent.

Only those masons who demonstrate skill at blueprint reading, working with and managing others, scheduling work, ordering materials and running a safe work site are promoted to foreman.

Where the Jobs Are

Although the demand for masons follows population growth, most of the work is in metropolitan areas, particularly in the suburbs, where office buildings, industrial parks and shopping centers are being built. Because the real estate business can flourish in one location for a time and then diminish, masons may have to move to a new town at least once in their lifetime to stay as busy as they want.

Training

Apprenticeship programs are generally sponsored by a local contractors' association or a labor-management committee. They usually last three years and teach skills you may not be exposed to by working for a single contractor, including setting terra-cotta (hardened clay tiles), ceramic tile block and artificial stone.

If you are turned down by the apprenticeship program committee, you may ask them if they will refer you to the Jobs Corps. If you qualify (you have to be from a low-income family, among other requirements) and are accepted into a Job Corps Center, you normally will be automatically accepted into a masonry apprenticeship program after your successful completion of the Job Corps program.

The Male/Female Equation

Of the five occupations discussed in this book, masonry has the fewest women—less than .2 percent. Much bricklaying and tile setting has far more to do with care, accuracy and an eye for beauty than with strength, which may attract more women to this trade.

Making Your Decision: What to Consider

The Bad News

- ❑ Much lifting and bending
- ❑ Working on scaffolding
- ❑ Hard on your hands
- ❑ Much of the work is repetitive

The Good News

- ❑ Strength is not a requirement for tile setting
- ❑ Little scaffold work for cement masons or terrazzo workers
- ❑ Outdoor work in good weather
- ❑ Possibility of good pay and overtime work

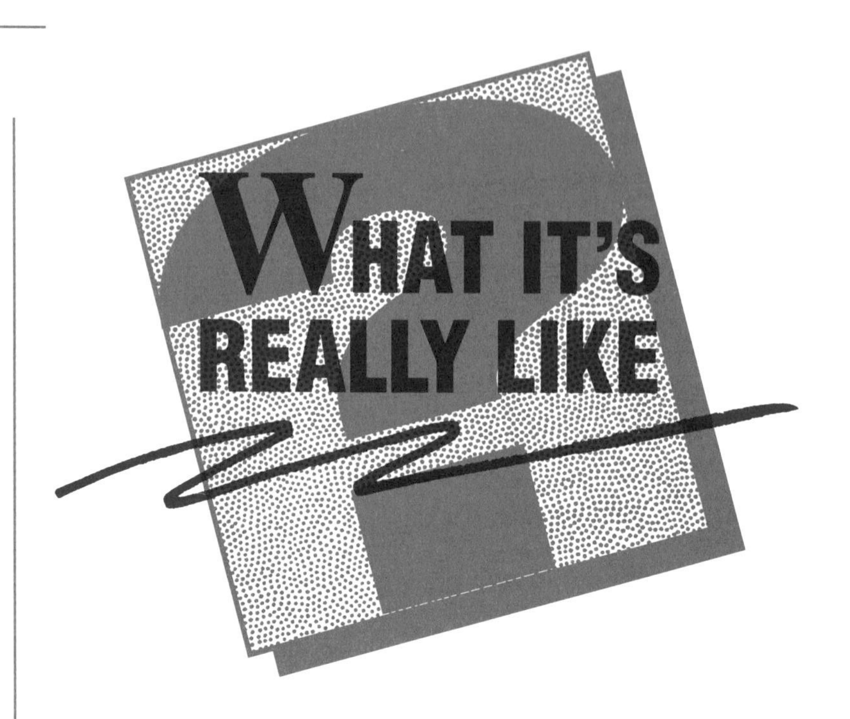

David Anderson, 29,
journeyman brickmason,
Febel Brothers Masonry,
Orland Park, Illinois
Years in the field: four

How did you get started in bricklaying?
A friend who was in the union told me about an opening in the apprenticeship program and how to apply. After taking an aptitude test and doing an interview, I started a 12-week course. I went every day from 8 to 4 and learned the skills of the trade. When I was finished, the union gave me job leads. I still work for the employer who first hired me. My boss put me on the line right away, laying brick. My apprenticeship lasted three years.

What kind of buildings do you work on?
Mostly industrial buildings. We lay one wall of cinder block and an exterior facing of brick. We do some houses, putting brick over wood frame and occasionally building fireplaces.

Is the work physically difficult?
I lift a lot and sometimes go home with a sore back. Also,

we're out in the weather. It gets hot and cold; I'm in the sun a lot.

How dangerous is your work?
We're up on scaffolds a lot, but they're safe. We wear hard hats when the job classification calls for it, and when we use a saw to cut the block or brick we wear safety goggles. Some guys are allergic to the lime in the mortar; they wear long sleeves to keep it off their skin.

What do you like most about your work?
Being outdoors. And I think the work is fun. Plus I'm out there with other guys, and we talk. You can get pretty close-knit with guys you're working with.

What do you like least about bricklaying?
The seasonal nature of it. When the temperature is below 30 degrees, or when it's going to rain all day, we can't work. No work, no money. And we have no paid vacations or paid sick leave. This past winter was a bad one, and we were off a lot.

Do you travel very far?
Most of the work I get is within a half hour's drive.

Do you or others moonlight other masonry jobs?
Our company doesn't mind if we take on some extra jobs, as long as it doesn't interfere with our regular work. The union doesn't particularly like us to work extra jobs on the weekends, but they don't really hassle us about it either.

What is it you are particularly proud of?
The quality of the work we do.

Do you have variety in your job?
Yes. We'll do buildings with arches and columns; we'll lay brick in a herringbone pattern, which is more than just laying brick in a line. We recently finished a banquet hall that had large arches. We've done some custom houses. We've done some chimneys with some pretty fancy tops, and that is very satisfying.

What advice would you give to someone considering going into bricklaying?
Try to get a summer job as a laborer with a masonry contractor to find out if you really want to do this. Remember

that it's critical to be dependable. Employers want people they can count on. If you're good to them, they'll try to be good to you.

Dennis Studley, 36, instructor and tile, terrazzo and marble setter, International Masonry Institute, San Bernardino, California Years in the field: 16

How did you get into this line of work?
I had been working as a purchasing agent for an electronics firm. My father-in-law was the superintendent for a tile contractor. He told me he needed a tile helper and offered me more money, so I became what's called an improver. It's like being an apprentice tile setter. You mix the mortar, carry tile, do the grouting and do the "go-fer" work.

What did you find difficult early on?
Getting in shape, because we do a lot of lifting. Also, it seemed I was always behind. The journeyman always worked faster than me, so I had to go back on Saturdays and grout the bathrooms I hadn't finished.

What sort of tile jobs did you work on?
The bathrooms—tubs and showers—in tract houses. I did this for two years and then moved from Arizona to San Bernardino, where I became a formal apprentice.

Did you get credit for the work you had done in Arizona?
Yes. And I began classes too. They taught me how to do floors, walls, countertops, archways and ceilings using ceramic tile, terrazzo and marble. I learned to read blueprints and brushed up on math. I went to class every other Saturday for eight hours a day, nine months a year.

How do you set tile in a bathroom?
Basically, it's spreading cement on the wall and then setting the tile into it. Afterward you apply grout into the spaces between tiles.

What about terrazzo and marble work?
Terrazzo can be hard on your back because you're working with a lot of concrete. You're laying out the concrete and troweling it properly, then washing away the thin upper layer to reveal the pebbles below. Marble we set in cement; on walls we suspend it with wires and set it in cement.

Have you done some interesting work with these materials?
I worked in Palm Springs for a time, where we did custom homes and laid marble floors and terrazzo pool decks and built marble fireplaces. We even made mailboxes and fences out of marble. We fabricate our marble in our own shop, round its edges and polish it.

What is the difference between tract, commercial and custom-home work?
Tract work is "get it up as quickly as you can." Commercial work involves shopping centers, schools and hotels. It's all laid out for you, and you have to hustle all day long. You have quotas. The spaces are all bigger—bigger walls, bigger floors. Custom work is for the fine homes. There, the rule is slow down and do it right.

Is the work particularly hazardous or uncomfortable?
I don't like heights and don't get up on scaffolding or ladders much. Your fingers do get dry from the cement, and some guys will come down with what we call "cement poisoning." It's an allergic reaction to cement that can get bad enough to end your career. We wear work boots and often goggles. Sometimes we wear hard hats. We're on our knees a lot.

What do you like most about tile, terrazzo and marble setting?
Getting to see the finished product. Driving past some custom houses and saying, "I did that."

What are you proudest of?
The marble and tile work I did for Frank Sinatra's house in Palm Springs.

What advice would you have for someone thinking about tile, terrazzo and marble setting as a career?
Take some blueprint reading, drafting and basic math. If

you're a woman, go for it. There are more women all the time. The work is not all that heavy. And the women seem to be more particular about how they do their work.

Fernando Posada, 31,
cement mason,
Hoffman Structures,
Rio Rancho, New Mexico
Years in the field: four

What does a cement mason do?
Makes sidewalks, driveways, floors, columns, parking garages, highways, anything made out of concrete.

What kind of work have you done lately?
Floors in commercial buildings and patching walls, meaning putting in new concrete where old has deteriorated. Also laying new large floors for a new factory.

How do you do a typical floor?
The forms are already in place. We oversee the concrete poured into the forms. We wear rubber boots and wade into the concrete to spread it around and level it out. We make sure it's at the proper height. Then we use a long board to get it roughly level. After that we use a bullfloat, a float with a long handle—because by this time we are not standing in the concrete anymore—to level it off even more. We wait for the concrete to stiffen some, and then we go out on it on knee boards and smooth it with a hand float and trowel. We wait for it to stiffen some more so we can walk on it. Then we use what is called a trowel machine, which resembles a large floor buffer. Finally, we wipe up wet or rough spots.

How big a crew do you work on?
Up to about 14 people. When we patch concrete, we might work alone.

How do you do patching?
We use a special mortar. We might work in older buildings where the concrete has been damaged, or we might be going into new buildings where other workers have not

done such a good job. We once worked six months patching a beautiful federal building in Oakland, California.

What other sorts of work have you done?
I've built sidewalks. I've made concrete stairs, which can be kind of tricky. I've also worked on highways, patching deteriorated parts and pouring new slab sections. But I didn't like the highway work because of the danger from cars.

Is your present work in any way dangerous?
Not really. We don't work on scaffolding, except for some patching jobs. Still, we wear hard hats, safety glasses and gloves to protect the skin on our hands. Concrete can dry your skin and irritate cuts.

How did you get started in concrete work?
My father was a cement mason. I used to help him, and he told me how to get into an apprenticeship program. In the beginning you really are a laborer. It's a pretty hard job. You shovel concrete, dig holes, pick up trash and wood.

How long was the apprenticeship program?
I went to class twice a month for three years. I learned math, the history of concrete, how to place concrete, how to repair small engines, how to use trowel machines and how to read blueprints. The classes also had hands-on work like building forms for stairs and floors. During this time I was being sent out to regular jobs by the union hall.

Did they ever send you out alone?
No. They always made sure three journeymen from the local went with you or were already on that job to help you. When they learned I was an apprentice, they would really be very nice and try to teach me well.

What do you consider hardest about being a cement mason?
The hours you can put in. When you work with concrete, you have to see it through to the end, because as soon as it's poured it starts hardening. You can't leave it. So if the concrete truck is late, say, or there is some other delay, you can be on the job long after regular quitting time. I've been on jobs until two or three o'clock in the morning.

What do you like most?
The satisfaction of seeing what you've done at the end of the day. To look at something done well and say, "I did that."

What advice would you give to someone considering becoming a cement mason?
Try to get a summer job with a construction company as a laborer to see what trade you like. I think cement masonry is a good trade if you like to work hard and learn. Once you are skilled, you can go into business for yourself as a contractor.

TIMBERLINE

You are up on the roof of an old house, prying off the worn shingles—dusty work. Then you lay down the new, better-made shingles. You cut metal flashing to put around the chimney and vent pipes. Slowly, surely, you lay the shingles up the slope of the roof. Finally you set the last shingles along the roof ridge. At day's end you look down. The new roof looks great, and the house is watertight.

Water damage is irritating and can threaten the value, even the existence, of a house or building. That's why roofing and waterproofing are such important trades. The work is exacting because even the smallest mistakes can allow moisture penetration.

Roofers work with all kinds of construction materials.

Composition shingles—a blend of fiberglass and asphalt—are commonly used on houses today, but roofers also work with clay tiles, metal shingles, metal strips, slate or roll roofing (shingles made of fiberglass and asphalt). On a shopping mall, skyscraper, factory or industrial park, roofers might work with hot asphalt, asphalt-impregnated paper (called roofing felt) or coatings made from liquidized plastic or rubber.

Roofers do more than fasten down roofing materials or spread the coatings. Much of the skilled work comes at the odd corners and protrusions of the roofs. At a chimney or plumbing vent, at eaves and the peaks of roofs or where two sections of roof meet (called a valley), roofers have to fashion roofing felt, shingles or strips of metal called flashing to make a waterproof seal against rain, ice and wind. Doing so often calls for sophisticated craftsmanship.

Some roofing work is repetitive—for example, laying the roofs of new houses in a development of similar architecture. But roofing can be extraordinary too; just ask the roofers who work on the steeple of a church or the heliport of a skyscraper.

A roofer has to learn to work ladders and hoists, to direct heavy bundles of roofing materials to the roof by crane and to move heavy bundles across the roof safely. Although there are precautions a roofer can take to make working on a pitched roof more manageable, the balancing act is still tricky. Roofing has the highest accident rate of any construction trade.

An offshoot of roofing often takes roofers to the foundation or basement. Here the work is waterproofing, to protect the building against water in the soil. Some large buildings have several stories underground, including parking garages, and all have to be guarded against moisture seepage. Foundation waterproofers use many of the same materials as a commercial roofer but do their work as the building is going up.

If heights, hard work and heavy lifting don't bother you, and the idea of being able to keep people "high and dry" appeals to you, you should consider roofing and waterproofing.

Getting into the Field

What You'll Learn

- ❏ Basic mathematics and mechanical drawing
- ❏ Different kinds of roofing, their advantages and disadvantages in given situations
- ❏ Types of fasteners and their suitability for use with different materials
- ❏ How to work safely on both flat and pitched roofs
- ❏ How to work with materials such as asphalt, tile and slate
- ❏ How to use hoists and cranes

Necessary Skills

- ❏ Tool know-how, particularly the use of hammers, saws and knives as well as power nailers
- ❏ Ability to safely set up scaffolding and hoists
- ❏ Ability to estimate roofing materials needed from the square footage of a roof

Do You Have What It Takes?

- ❏ No fear of heights
- ❏ Tolerance for heat from dark roofs on hot days
- ❏ Ability to withstand the strong odor of hot bitumen (a type of asphalt)
- ❏ Willingness to work in all kinds of weather

Physical Requirements

- ❏ Better-than-average upper-body strength
- ❏ Good physical condition
- ❏ Good sense of balance
- ❏ Ability to tolerate bending, climbing and kneeling

Apprenticeship Program Requirements

- ❏ 18 years of age (most states)
- ❏ High school diploma or general equivalency diploma (GED) helpful but not essential
- ❏ Good physical health

Licenses Required

Contractors, but not their employees, need to be licensed. A roofer may have to be certified in safety procedures if working on a roof containing hazardous substances such as asbestos.

Job Outlook

Job openings will grow: about as fast as average

The need for roofers is less tied to booms in new construction than are other construction trades because much roofing work is replacement and repair on existing structures. (Roofs wear out faster than most components of a building.)

The Ground Floor

Entry-level jobs: apprentice, helper, laborer

On-the-Job Responsibilities

Beginners

- ❑ Carry shingles and rolls of roofing materials up ladders
- ❑ Set up ladders, scaffolding and hoists
- ❑ Clean company trucks, take inventory of roofing materials
- ❑ Measure and cut materials for others
- ❑ Install shingles or tiles
- ❑ Learn about different roofing and waterproofing materials and how to install them

Experienced Roofers

May do any of the above, plus:

- ❑ Cut and install the flashing for valleys and vents
- ❑ Become the foreman on a crew
- ❑ Become self-employed and hire other roofers

Waterproofers

- ❑ Prep the surface of concrete
- ❑ Remove all dirt with wire brushes, sanders and grinders
- ❑ Use brushes or rollers to apply a primer and then waterproofing and protection board

When You'll Work

Even though your contract with an employer may call for a 35- or 40-hour workweek, you may be asked to work longer hours—including evenings and weekends—to meet a deadline.

Time Off

Roofers work when weather conditions permit—rain and extremely cold weather mean no work. Most union roofers and waterproofers get major holidays off. You can take vacations when your work schedule permits.

Perks

- ❑ Use of the company truck (some employers)
- ❑ Use of tools
- ❑ Access to sheet metal shops
- ❑ Health insurance and paid vacation (some employers)

Who's Hiring

- ❑ Roofing contractors
- ❑ Waterproofing contractors
- ❑ General contractors

Places You'll Go

Beginners and experienced roofers: Some potential for travel

Most work is within a 200-mile radius of the contractor's office.

Surroundings

Residential roofers work mainly on pitched roofs. They mount ladders or scaffolding and often work with their feet set against braces temporarily nailed to the roofs. Commercial roofers generally work on flat roofs—sometimes on buildings only a few stories high, sometimes on skyscrapers. Although they have less risk of falling, they often work with hot bitumen that can burn as well as smell bad. In addition, on hot days the black roofing material gets very hot underfoot. Both types of roofers work outdoors and in nearly all kinds of weather.

On-the-Job Hazards

- ❑ Falls from scaffolding, ladders and roofs
- ❑ Burns from hot bitumen
- ❑ Cuts from saws and knives and injuries from hammers
- ❑ Heat prostration on hot days
- ❑ Allergic reaction to sulfur in old roofing

Dollars and Cents

Hourly pay: $10-$30
Average national hourly pay: $18

Time and a half for overtime is common; your hourly rate may be even higher if the work falls on a holiday or a Sunday. Apprentices begin earning half of a journeyman's wage; they usually make about 90 percent of a journeyman's wage after 30 months.

Moving Up

Employers are always on the lookout for employees who can motivate others to do their work better and faster, so if you have good people and management skills you may be tapped to become a foreman. Foremen may have one roofer or scores of roofers under their direction.

Foremen who are good at what they do may go on to become superintendents, who go from job site to job site checking on the work. A roofer may also become an estimator, helping the employer bid on jobs, or an office manager.

Another option for experienced roofers is opening their own business: one in three do so and usually specialize in residential roofing.

Where the Jobs Are

Roofing work is generally best in places where there is new construction, although a certain amount of roofing involves replacement of old roofs. Urban centers offer the most roofing work. Suburban or outlying areas are good because shopping malls, industrial parks and homes are often under construction. When the economy takes a nose-dive, many homeowners hire roofers to patch rather than replace their roofs.

Training

A Joint Apprenticeship Training Committee made up of contractors and unions runs a three-year apprenticeship program. Joining one gives you the surest route to broad skills; learning on the job outside an apprenticeship program may limit your skills to the one or two kinds of roofing and waterproofing your employer does. The program generally includes 144 hours of classroom work. Normally, an apprenticeship program lasts three years.

The Male/Female Equation

Women represent less than .5 percent of all roofers.

Making Your Decision: What to Consider

The Bad News

- ❏ Most hazardous type of construction work
- ❏ Exposure to bad odors when working with hot asphalt
- ❏ Lots of lifting and bending
- ❏ Layoffs in bad weather

The Good News

- ❏ High turnover, so there's more of a chance to break in
- ❏ Working outside in good weather
- ❏ Re-roofing can create work when new roofing jobs fall off
- ❏ Good opportunities for going into business for yourself

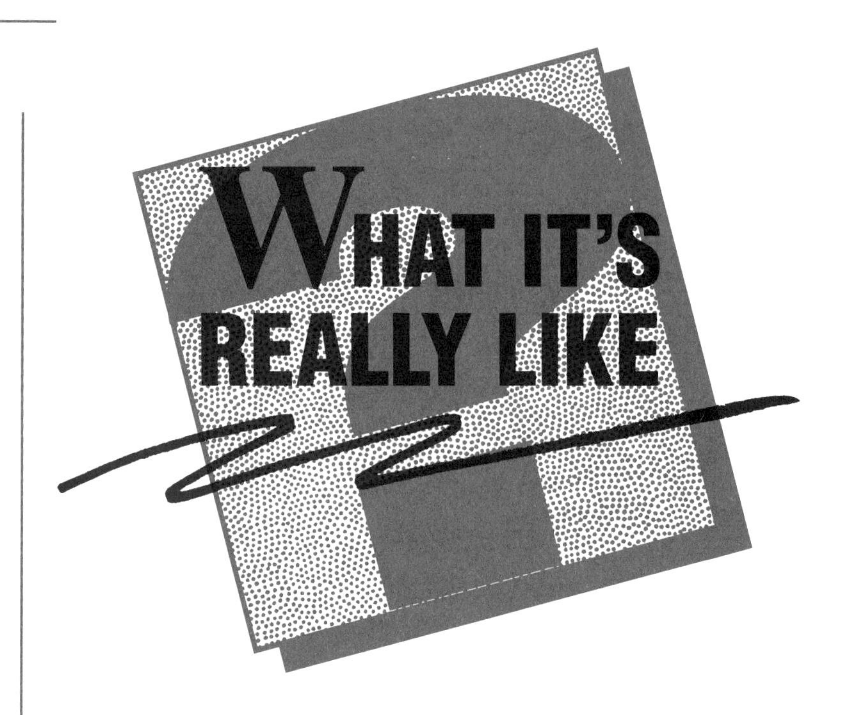

Doug Andersen, 35,
commercial roofer,
McDowall Company,
St. Cloud, Minnesota
Years in the field: seven

Did you go right into roofing from high school?
No. I drove a truck, worked in a factory and did some house framing. Then a friend told me that a commercial roofing company was looking for roofers. I joined as a pre-apprentice.

What did you do?
I helped the journeyman roofers. I did sweeping, lifting and cleaning and got materials. I was a pre-apprentice for about half a year. Then I joined the union program. It lasted for 5,000 hours of work. Now I'm a journeyman.

What was the classroom work like?
We went to four or five training sessions each winter, when the work is slow here. Because I was working for a commercial roofer and wanted to go into commercial roofing, most of my sessions were about commercial roofing.

Were you tested often?
We'd have one three-hour exam—much of which covered safety issues—at the end of each winter training session. If you do the assignments, you don't have trouble.

What were your early months as an apprentice like?
Of the 65 who joined at the same time I did, only three were left at the end of the first year. Some didn't like the coal tar or pitch roofs with a high sulfur content. When this roofing material is cut, ripped or torn off, the fine particles get into your skin and create burning and irritation. You have to dress in long sleeves and a hard hat and wear safety glasses. And you have to learn not to touch your skin until the tear-off is all done and you can wash up with plenty of soap and water.

What was most difficult for you in the first year?
Some of the journeymen you're working for can be pretty demanding. And working in weather extremes was rough.

Do heights bother you?
Not on flat roofs; generally they are only a couple of stories high. On a sloped roof, I'd just as soon be on a safety line.

What sort of work do you currently do?
Nearly all commercial work, from gas stations to industrial parks, with an occasional house thrown in. When we put down a new roof, about half the time it's rubber sheeting and half the time it's hot asphalt. We start out by putting down the type of insulation the architects have called for. With asphalt, you begin heating it to 450 degrees. Then you spread it with a mop and lay hardboard insulation on top. You might do a couple of layers of this and finish off with four plys of fiberglass felt. With rubber, the insulation is usually loose-laid, and then a sheet of rubber is rolled on top. The rubber sheeting is held down by gravel or by securing strips at the edges of the roof.

How long was it before you felt you had mastered your skill?
About three years, but I'm still learning, and I'm still going to training sessions held by materials manufacturers.

Is there variety in your work?
Yes. I have a knack for repair and leaks work, which requires patience and problem-solving ability. About 70 percent of my time is spent working by myself or with one or two other guys checking out leaks or making repairs. It's possible to be working on a single new roofing job for a couple of months, but I tend to be in one place one day and another the next.

What do you like least about commercial roofing?
The fact that you can be laid off a lot in the winter. That makes it sort of feast or famine during some seasons. I'm paid by the hour, and I tend not to work much overtime.

What are you proudest of in your work?
The fact that I work for a company that delivers on its promises to customers, that goes the extra mile for them.

Wiley Bateman, 33,
waterproofer and roofer,
Haight Roofing Company,
Ballard, Washington
Years in the field: five

What does a waterproofer do?
Waterproofers are called in whenever surfaces that are underground have to be protected against penetration by water. Normally these are concrete walls and floors. A good example is the levels of underground parking garages of buildings. Waterproofers seal them against moisture. The seal is so good, it will last longer than the concrete itself.

How do you do it?
First we prep the surface of the concrete. We remove all dirt with wire brushes, sanders and grinders. Next we use brushes or rollers to apply a primer that soaks up whatever dirt and dust we missed. Then we apply the waterproofing. It's called monolithic rubberized membrane, and it comes in 55-gallon drums. We heat it in a kettle to about 400 degrees, then apply it to the primed surface. We have to use just the right amount, and we have to make sure that we are not leaving any air bubbles.

The last thing we do is apply protection board. It's one-eighth-inch-thick board that is smooth on the side that goes against the membrane we've applied and rough on the other side. It protects the membrane from rough dirt, pebbles, rocks, roots, that sort of thing.

Do you work on things other than the underground portion of buildings?
I worked for a year and a half on the I-90 tunnel. It was five and a half miles long.

How did you get into this line of work?
I got out of the military in 1990. My brother was a roofer. He told me how I could get into an apprenticeship program through the union. Three days after I applied, I got a job and was enrolled in the apprenticeship program.

How long was the program, and what did you do in it?
It's a two-year program, but it took me a little longer because weather did not allow me to work as many hours as I needed to complete the program in exactly two years. We went to class one night a week. There we learned safety and basic roofing and waterproofing, but learning was on-the-job.

How much of your work now is roofing?
I usually work about nine and a half months at waterproofing and the rest at commercial roofing. I've helped put roofs in Boeing factories and on many of the major buildings in Seattle.

Do you travel much?
Up to about 100 miles. I've been to Vancouver, British Columbia, on jobs and to Olympia, Washington. When we go that far, we usually stay for a week and drive back weekends.

Is the work physically demanding?
Roofing is hard work because you are lifting a lot, and you bend over and stay bent over a lot.

What do you like most about your job?
Doing it, finishing it and later never hearing the phone ring, meaning the general contractor was satisfied with our work.

What advice would you give someone considering going into this trade?
You'll see hard times and you'll see good times, but the hard times will come first. Some days you'll not want to go to class after a tough day's work. But if you stick with it, it will pay off for you.

Don Guest Jr., 29,
roofer and sheet metal worker,
Bob Hilson & Co.,
Miami, Florida
Years in the field: 15

When did you get started in roofing?
My father was a roofer, so I worked for him during summers. When I dropped out of high school, I worked for him full time. I then went into the service, came out, got my general equivalency diploma (GED) and went back to work for him. Now I work for another roofing company.

What did you do early on?
I put up scaffolding, carried materials, cleaned out trucks and cleaned the warehouse.

Did you do most of your learning on the job?
Yes, most of it. I learned from the more experienced people. After about a year as a laborer, I began tearing off old roofs and putting on new roofing materials. Much of the sheet metal work I now do I taught myself.

Did you ever have any formal training?
Yes. I joined something called the Pride Program, organized by the local roofing and sheet metal contractors association. We went to classes one night a week for eight weeks to learn safety, characteristics of insulation, waterproofing, the thermal compatibility of differing materials and more.

What were you doing when you first started out on roofs?
I worked on a large townhouse and condominium project that required tile roofs for a couple of years, setting the tile

and doing the flashing (the metal strips where roof sections come together or meet a vertical wall).

Did you like the tile work?
It was hard on my back. We'd lift about four tons of tile a day, plus more than a ton of mortar that we set it in.

What other sorts of work have you done?
I've done tear-offs; that's when we rip off the old roofing. It's hardest taking off metal roofing because you have to pull out each nail. Shingle and wood shakes are easier because you can use a tool like a squared-off shovel to pry them off.

Are you bothered by heights or any other aspect of roofing?
Heights don't bother me a bit. At first the smell of hot tar can bother you, but you get used to it. You have to be careful of the heat and sun, and when you are working with sheet metal, you have to have good eyewear to protect you from glare. When we do tear-offs, it can get dusty. We wear a special cream when there might be fiberglass blowing around.

Have you ever been hurt?
I've never fallen off a roof. But I fell through one once; the wood below was rotten. I wasn't hurt and went right back to work.

What do you like most about roofing work?
I like to be outside in the fresh air and working with people who are knowledgeable. I like taking something that is flat and shaping it into something useful that you know will be there for many years. I like leaving a little bit of me behind.

What do you like least about the work?
Trying to convince others that they should be doing something they really don't want to do. I also much prefer the sheet metal work to the hot tar or shingle work, both of which are repetitive and boring.

What are you especially proud of?
Shaping the metal I work with. On each roofing job there is a place that calls for a unique piece of metal. I have to make a little piece of art right there on the spot. I've

worked on national monuments, on famous people's homes, on great estates and old churches. I'm proud of that work.

What advice would you give to someone considering roofing?
Stick with math. If you want to get into a higher level of sheet metal work and flashing, you have to know how to solve problems with geometry and trigonometry.

MORE INFORMATION PLEASE

If you complete a union-affiliated apprenticeship program, you are not required to join the union when you gain journeyman status. On rare occasions, there may be a clause in your apprenticeship enrollment contract that says if you leave the union within a certain number of years (typically four), you may have to pay back some portion of your training. If you complete a non-union-affiliated apprenticeship program and want to join a union, you can usually do so if there are openings. You may also be asked to take a portion of the union's program to ensure that you meet its standards of craftsmanship.

Carpenter

Apprenticeship and Training Department
United Brotherhood of Carpenters and Joiners of America
101 Constitution Avenue, NW
Washington, D.C. 20001
202-546-6206

Write or call for the six-page booklet *Apprenticeship in the Building and Construction Trades.*

Manpower and Training Services
Associated General Contractors of America
1957 E. Street, NW
Washington, D.C. 20006
202-393-2040

Education Department
Associated Builders & Contractors
1300 N. 17th Street
Rosslyn, Virginia 22209
703-812-2000

Call or write the two organizations listed above for information on non-union commercial carpentry and masonry apprenticeship programs.

Electrician

Independent Electrical Contractors (IEC)
P.O. Box 10379
Alexandria, Virginia 22310-0379
703-549-7351

Call or write for information on non-union apprenticeship programs.

National Joint Apprenticeship and Training Committee
16201 Trade Zone Avenue, #105
Upper Marlboro, Maryland 20772
301-249-2042

Write or call for the 16-page brochure *Electrical Apprenticeship.*

Plumber

National Association of Plumbing-Heating-Cooling Contractors (NAPHCC)
P.O. Box 6808
Falls Church, Virginia 22046
703-237-8100

Training Department
United Association of Journeymen and Apprentices of the Plumbing and Pipefitting Industry of the U.S. and Canada
901 Massachusetts Avenue, NW
Washington, D.C. 20001
202-628-5823

Write or call for information about apprenticeship programs. You can also call or write the Joint Apprenticeship Committees run by the union local and local affiliates of these organizations.

Mason

International Masonry Institute
823 15th Street, NW, Suite 1001
Washington, D.C. 20005
202-383-3908

Write or call for information on union apprenticeship programs. You can also contact Associated General Contractors of America or Associated Builders & Contractors (see addresses above, under Carpenter) for information on non-union apprenticeship programs.

Roofer/Waterproofer

United Union of Roofers, Waterproofers and Allied Workers
1125 17th Street, NW
Washington, D.C. 20036
202-638-3228

Write for a brochure called *Roofing and Waterproofing: A Trade Worth Learning Through Apprenticeship.*

National Roofing Contractors Association
10255 Higgins Road
Rosemont, Illinois 60018
708-299-9070

Call or write the publications department for career information.

All Trades

Home Builders Institute
1090 Vermont Avenue, NW
Washington, D.C. 20005
202-371-0600

Write or call for information on non-union residential apprenticeship programs.

WILL YOU FIT INTO THE BUILDING WORLD?

Before you sign up for an apprenticeship program or start to look for one of the jobs described in this book, it's smart to figure out whether that trade will be a good fit given your background, skills and personality. There are several ways to do that, including:

- ❑ Talk to people who already work in that field. Find out what they like and don't like about their jobs, what kinds of people their employers hire, and what their recommendations are about training. Ask them if there are any books or publications that would be helpful for you to read. Maybe you could even "shadow" the workers for a day as they go about their duties.
- ❑ Use a computer to help you identify career options. Some of the most widely used software programs are *Discover,* by the American College Testing Service; *SIGI Plus,* developed by the Educational Testing Service; and *Careers,* by Peterson's. Some public libraries make this career software available to library users at little or no cost. The career counseling or guidance office of your high school or local community college is another possibility.
- ❑ Take a vocational interest test. The most common are the Strong Interest Inventory and the Kuder

Occupational Interest Survey. High schools and colleges usually offer free testing to students and alumni at their guidance and career-planning offices. Many career counselors in private practice or at community job centers can also give the test and interpret the results.

- ❑ Talk to a career counselor. You can find one by asking friends and colleagues if they know of any good ones. Or contact the career information office in the adult education division of a local college. Its staff and workshop leaders often do one-on-one counseling. The job information services division of major libraries sometimes offers low- or no-cost counseling by appointment. Or check the *Yellow Pages* under the heading "Vocational Guidance."

  But first, before you spend time, energy or money doing any of the above, take one or more of the following five quizzes (one for each career discussed in the book). The results can help you begin to evaluate whether you have the basic traits and abilities that are important to success in that career—in short, whether you are cut out for it.

If becoming a carpenter interests you, take this quiz:

Read each statement, then rate how you feel about it by choosing number 0, 5 or 10 according to the following scale:

0 = Disagree
5 = Agree somewhat
10 = Strongly agree

___I enjoy the smell and feel of wood
___I enjoy making things with hand and power tools
___I take great satisfaction in seeing the physical results of my work and seeing a job through from start to finish
___I can readily solve problems with fractions
___I like to pay attention to detail and see things come out right
___I have good balance and don't mind heights

___I don't mind working outside even in harsh weather
___I can handle the idea of working long hours when necessary to meet a deadline
___I have good communication skills and work easily with others
___I have good eye-hand coordination

Now add up your score. ___Total points

If your total points are less than 50, you probably don't have sufficient interest in carpentry or the inclination to learn what's required. If your total points are between 50 and 75, you may have what it takes to get into the field, but be sure to spend time as a helper to make sure the work is right for you. If your total points are 75 or more, it's highly likely that you are a good candidate for a career as a carpenter.

If becoming an electrician interests you, take this quiz:

Read each statement, then rate how you feel about it by choosing number 0, 5 or 10 according to the following scale:

0 = Disagree
5 = Agree somewhat
10 = Strongly agree

___I like to tinker with electric appliances, motors and toys
___I'm good at math and can use logic to solve problems
___I'm good at taking precautions and following rules in dangerous situations
___I'm the kind of person who will redo something if I don't think I've done it right the first time
___I like working with hand and power tools
___Crawling through dark or cramped spaces wouldn't bother me
___I don't mind working with large power tools
___I have good balance and don't have a fear of heights

___I have good eyesight and color vision and a good sense of smell

___I have good study habits and the determination to learn electrical and building codes

Now add up your score. ___Total points

If your total points are less than 50, you probably don't have sufficient interest or determination to make it in an electrical apprenticeship program. If your total points are between 50 and 75, you may have what it takes to get into the field and make it as an electrician, but be sure to double-check your choice by working as a helper. If your total points are 75 or more, it's highly likely that you are right on track to find success and satisfaction as an electrician.

If becoming a plumber interests you, take this quiz:

Read each statement, then rate how you feel about it by choosing number 0, 5 or 10 according to the following scale:

0 = Disagree
5 = Agree somewhat
10 = Strongly agree

___I have a good mechanical aptitude

___The idea of using my ingenuity and skills to solve a problem appeals to me

___I wouldn't mind being on call for emergency repairs if it meant a good financial reward

___I have the determination and study habits to master public health and plumbing codes

___I have an easygoing personality and don't mind working for difficult clients

___I am a very safety-conscious person

___I have better-than-average upper-body strength and a strong back

___I have no phobias about heights or confined spaces

___I have good finger dexterity (ability to work with small parts)

___I enjoy working with tools

Now add up your score. ___Total points

If your total points are less than 50, you probably don't have sufficient interest in plumbing or the inclination to learn what's required. If your total points are between 50 and 75, you may do well in an apprenticeship program, but first decide if that's for you by becoming a plumber's helper. If your total points are 75 or more, it's highly likely that you are a good candidate for a career as a plumber.

If becoming a mason interests you, take this quiz:

Read each statement, then rate how you feel about it by choosing number 0, 5 or 10 according to the following scale:

0 = Disagree
5 = Agree somewhat
10 = Strongly agree

___I would get great satisfaction from using materials to build long-lasting structures
___I don't mind intense physical labor
___I enjoy working outdoors and can withstand weather extremes
___I have above-average strength and stamina
___I have a good sense for what is pleasing to the eye
___I can work well with others to get a job done
___I am comfortable using hand and power tools
___I have a good eye for detecting what is level and plumb (straight up and down)
___I can handle working in a dusty place and can tolerate dry, raw skin
___I can do manual work that requires precision and an eye for detail

Now add up your score. ___Total points

If your total points are less than 50, you probably don't have the physical characteristics or mind-set to make it as a mason. If your total points are between 50 and 75, you may be a good candidate for this field, but find out first whether you can pass the test of being a laborer. If your total points are 75 or more, it's highly likely that you have all the "right stuff" to be successful as a mason.

If becoming a roofer interests you, take this quiz:

Read each statement, then rate how you feel about it by choosing number 0, 5 or 10 according to the following scale:

0 = Disagree
5 = Agree somewhat
10 = Strongly agree

___I don't mind heights and have good balance
___I believe in taking precautions so accidents don't happen
___I don't mind lifting and carrying heavy loads
___I could handle periods of unemployment
___I have strong math skills to solve roofing problems
___I know how to use tools and enjoy working with them
___I feel I could learn to do accurate materials estimates
___I can stand the strong odor of hot bitumen (a type of asphalt)
___I am willing to work outside in all kinds of weather
___I can tolerate a lot of bending, climbing and kneeling

Now add up your score. ___Total points

If your total points are less than 50, you probably don't have what it takes to make it as a roofer. If your total points are between 50 and 75, you may meet the physical demands of the job, but find out if you like the work itself by becoming a helper. If your total points are 75 or more, it's highly likely that you will do well as a roofer.

ABOUT THE AUTHOR

Brooke C. Stoddard has been a freelance writer since 1983. Before going out on his own, he worked as a writer and editor for Time-Life Books, where he wrote books on home improvement, World War II and computers. He has written news, commentary and travel stories for the *Washington Post* and cover stories and other pieces for the regional magazine *Mid-Atlantic Country;* his work has also appeared in the *Baltimore Sun* and the *Chicago Sun-Times.* He has written about law for *Everyday Law* and about computer technology for several computer publications, including *Government Computer News* and *Washington Technology.*

In the field of construction, he has written stories for *Historic Preservation* and *Construction Specifier* magazines. He co-authored *A Consumer's Guide to Home Improvement, Renovation and Repair* (John Wiley & Sons, 1990), which became a Book-of-the-Month Club Alternate Selection and a selection of three other book clubs.

Other topics he has covered with regularity are manufacturing, the natural gas industry, credit union policy, local government finance, urban planning, federal government technology policy and family finance. He is currently at work on a book about steel making.